First published in England in 1992
Reprinted 1995

Copyright © by J. L. Carr

ISBN 0 900847 93 X

THE QUINCE TREE PRESS
BURY ST EDMUNDS
01284 753228

HARPOLE & FOXBERROW
GENERAL PUBLISHERS
A BUSINESS HISTORY (WITH FOOTNOTES)

The woodcut on the cover is by Ian Stephens of Northampton. The singing birds are Joan Hassall's. George Cruikshank drew the printing-press and proof on the front-cover endpiece. Garamond type was used for the main text.

By the same author
Novels

Available in Quince Tree Press Editions

Social History

For Children

The green children of the woods – *Longman*
The Red Windcheater – *Macmillan*
and others

This is a Printing Office,
Cross-roads of Civilisation,
Refuge of all the Arts against the Ravages of Time.
From this place Words may fly abroad
Not to perish as Waves of Sound but fix'd in Time,
Not corrupted by the hurrying Hand but verified in Proof.
Friend, you are on Safe Ground:
This is a Printing Office.

Photoset and printed in Great Britain by
Stanley L. Hunt (Printers) Ltd. Rushden, Northamptonshire

For Heulwen who checked the proofs and
for Mrs Widmerpool's sister who asked "What *are* books?
Where do they come from?" and
for that Mr Williams who was "ridiculously ill-equipped
for the book-trade, having read most of the books
he was trying to sell and ever ready to discuss
literature even with those using his premises
for a free read". And,
uncharitably, for burners of books they won't or can't read.

James Lloyd Carr was born in 1912, attended the village school
at Carlton Miniott in the North Riding and Castleford Secondary
School. He died in Northamptonshire in 1994.

What went ye out into the wilderness to see? A reed shaken with the wind?

Matthew, Chapter 11, v. 7.

What though my wealth be trash,
The heart is true,
The heart is true.

John Dowland, Song.

People think because a novel's invented, it isn't true. Exactly the reverse is the case. Because a novel's invented, it is true.

X. Trapnel, novelist, in
Anthony Powell's *Hearing Secret Harmonies.*

Business, you know, may bring money but friendship hardly ever does.

Jane Austen, *Emma.*

These people appear elsewhere,

Mossop and Colonel Hebron may be found in *A Month in the Country.* Mr Gidner (senior) tells the story of *The Battle of Pollocks Crossing.* Mr Fangfoss, Nobbut Beatie, Doctor Kossuth, Alex and Diana Slingsby, Ginchy Montagu appear in *How Steeple Sinderby Wanderers won the F.A. Cup* which was written by George Gidner (junior). The young George Harpole and Emma Foxberrow are the chief concern of *The Harpole Report* and are supported by Edwin Shutlanger and his errant wife, Mrs Widmerpool's sister, Titus Fawcett, Emily Billitt, the Big Sixth Former, Mr Pintle, Grace Tollemache and Croser. An aged George Harpole and Miss Foxberrow meet finally in *What Hetty Did,* the tale of her struggles told by 18 year-old Hetty Beaumont.

FOREWORD

My first job was teaching games and Eng. lit. in a Hampshire school. The class knew by heart 'The Lady of Shalott' and could explain [to my satisfaction] what Robt. Browning had in mind when he wrote 'Karshish, the picker-up of Learning's crumbs, an Epistle'. I awaited a first inspection of my labours with a quiet confidence.

The Headmaster picked up the book. 'Ah!' he said, 'A book! Turn to page (i)'. They turned to Page One. 'Ah, no!' he said patiently, 'Not Page One. Page (i). And tell me who are Faber & Faber. Is he, they, one man or two men or perhaps Mrs & Mr Faber? Is he or they this book's author? And is a person who makes a book a bookmaker? What does ISBN mean and how should I say it? Is © a friend of the author? Is the book dedicated to him? Who are Butler & Tanner of Frome? What is a preface, an epigraph? This Foreword ··· need I read it? Can only William Shakespeare own a folio. Does a quire have a conductor? Can one catch a colophon by too heavy reading late at night? And spell it.'

He went on and on: my class's ignorance was utter. Finally, he pronounced sentence. 'You don't seem to know much about this book. And I haven't got as far as Page One..' My pupils looked reproachfully at me. Until that unnerving day I had supposed a book was a cosy arrangement between writer and reader.

And, of course, the brute was infuriatingly right. Books concern printers, publishers, sales reps, booksellers, proof-readers, professors, illustrators, indexers, critics, text editors, literary editors, librarians, book-reviewers and bookbinders and book-keepers, translators, typographers, Oxfam-fundraisers, whole university departments of soothsayers, manufacturers of thread and glue, auctioneers, lumberjacks, starving mice, wolves howling at the doors of authors of first-novels, the Post offices' book-bashing machine minder, religious bonfire fuel suppliers and libel-lawyers. And that this army is ~~camped upon~~ billeted upon one man or one woman gnawing a pen is neither here nor there.

So, by and large, this is what this book is about. It tries to answer Mrs Widmerpool's sister's alarming enquiry at George Harpole's trial, 'What are books? Where do they come from?'

Her 'Where do they go to?' is unanswerable ··· except, quite often — to the head.

James Carr.

By the Nine Gods he swore it and named a trysting day
And bade his messengers ride forth to summon his array.

It may seem to you, as it does to me, that as many hapless enterprises succeed as those scrupulously planned. And so it was with Harpole & Foxberrow, General Publishers. The firm's beginning was accidental, its progress haphazard, its end hastened not by commercial incompetence but by a spiritual ennui – as though the heart had gone out of it. A final memo from George Harpole supports my view,

> Hetty dear, You ask what brought things to a finish. Well . . . I'm not sure. Anyway, not absolutely sure. You see one thing seemed to spring from another as though, in its ups and downs, our little business had a mind of its own. As often as not, we didn't need to agonize over decisions: inevitably there was no other course but to hang on and hope all would be well. Then, without breast-beating, heart-burning, it came to a full-stop. And no one seemed to mind . . .
>
> Anyway, that's how I saw it. Of course I can't answer for Emma. Who could? Emma was Emma. Need I say more?

After the partners' expulsion from Sinji College of Almost Instant Teacher Training – at the diktat of an affronted Zanzambanian President* and with no more than a couple of hours' notice – each went off to a parental home, Miss Foxberrow to Oldheading Manor, Glos. and Harpole to

---

* The expulsion was provoked by their students' prolonged laughter when the President began his speech, "At this meaningful moment in time as life in the west finalizes and grinds to a halt, at the end of the day a shortfall. . . ." It seems that Miss Foxberrow, their Principal, had taught that any person uttering even one of these phrases immediately could be written off as "a self-opinionated windbag with a 4th-rate mind".

Dovecot Farm, up north near Wetherby. Both had resolved to have nothing more to do with education (let alone schools), Then, for several months, there was no communication between them. Emma Foxberrow would be aged about 33 and George Harpole, 35.

But, after delivering some bullocks to Knaresborough Cattle Mart, Harpole ran into an old grammar school acquaintance, now employed as a public librarian.* And he, learning that G.H. was at a loose end and not dead-set on farming, drew his notice to a minimum-rate classified ad in *The Booktrader,*

> *FOR SALE.* Rural jobbing-print business with some book-publishing Midlands. Adjacent accommodation. Steady income. Owner retiring (health). Reply Harold Blow. Offers.

MEMO (HARPOLE)

Alf told me this ad had run several weeks and recalled Blow kicking off with an asking-price of £24,000 for Goodwill with Equipment and Book stock at valuation. ("Didn't say whose valuation!") Went on to hint that continuing solicitation betokened no takers, so that Blow despairingly had sunk to "Offers".

Shouldn't have given it a second thought had not E.F.† written out of the blue saying she'd got her post-Sinji wind back and had I any bright ideas? As far as I recall, I was still fed-up at what went wrong between the two of us in those last African weeks, so didn't answer. Just sent her *The Booktrader* cutting.

---

* Alfred Neethe, later elected (by acclamation) President of the Library Workers Guild, after an AGM outburst from the floor nominating all authors as "whingeing self-promoting parasites" and hailing the dawn of that day when "book-writing machines will be standard library equipment so that *we* can programme books which *we* know our customers really want to read".

† Frith's *Tendencies in 20th Century Publishing* describes Emma Foxberrow as "an optimist in a predominately pessimistic profession".

Predictably, Miss Foxberrow's reading of the ad's portents was very different. She immediately demanded details and, significantly, Blow's reply is the earliest surviving item in the firm's files.

HAROLD BLOW, JOBBING PRINTER ALSO PUBLISHER.
POSTERS, HANDBILLS.
24 HOUR DELIVERY WEDDING AND
FUNERAL SERVICE SHEETS.

Dear Madam

Mrs Blow having been left a bungalow adjacent to the front at Birchington-upon-Sea, Kent, by her uncle-by-marriage (deceased) and her sister Aggie* residing at Westgate-upon-Sea, Kent, Mrs Blow is desirous to move nearer to her the sooner the better. I left off the printing when hot-metal went out and litho came in and me growing no younger. The old Invicta Press is in good trim also three fonts, Baskerville, Gill Sans, Caslon, also boxwood caps suited to election and auction bills, the same in Olde Englishe for Sacred Concerts, Xmas Bazaars and the Antiques Trade. Also I can fix up with my landlord Mr Fangfoss for incomer to take on leasehold, the rent being same these past 20 years money being nothing to him. Also three good-sized bedrooms and couple of attics, h & c, indoor *WC* also night-soil closet needing attention down the garden. Also cellars one in one out both dry, also paddock and orchard the latter run down. Also useful out-buildings.

Miss Foxberrow drove across from her Cotswold home, checked and qualified this information and, having paid a nominal £100 for goodwill, bought up Blow, lock, stock and barrel, for what she claimed was a more than generous £7,863. Her sole concession was to reluctantly promise

* Agnes Smithley, employed by Emerson-Buettner as an office-cleaner, later used the firm's computer to hack £2m from The Elver Valley Building Society before removing to a S. Honduras citrus plantation.

employment (subject to our satisfaction) to Blow's 18-year-old son, Albert, who didn't want to leave the district, he having a sweetheart (subject to *his* satisfaction).

EMMA FOXBERROW TO GEORGE HARPOLE

. . . Blow is a square-shaped breathless chap with overlong arms, a sort of aboriginal Caxton. Instead of putting his best foot forward and showing off his property to advantage, he endlessly drivelled on about his reluctance to leave Jordans Bank. Told me he detested southerners, the seaside and (particularly) his sister-in-law.

Mrs Blow, a miserable whingeing disloyal creature, is set on a remove the better to carry on (at closer quarters) a womb-feud with her twin sister, Agnes. Took me aside to whine, "You can't know what a relief it will be to flit from this dump, Miss. Round here they'll never let us forget what Harold* got up to all them years since, though he was nobbut seventeen at the time and isn't that way inclined anymore, not that he ever did what they say he did. Nowadays books is his only vice. Mind you, I like a book in the house: I sleep better."

House is pleasant enough . . . Edwardian brick . . . Pioneer Villa (prophetic?) Stands at edge of Jordans Bank (it being no more than a straggle of bankrupt builders' stock). It runs to a couple of places of worship, a post-office-shop and a desperate looking pub smelling of bilge-water.

Come on now. Put Sinji behind you. Stop reproaching yourself. It wasn't your doing that things went wrong. *Remember the good times.* (Those nights by the lagoon! That sandbar!) I'm moving in on May 20th. Come and help me.

---

* Whilst serving his apprenticeship it had been Blow's job to check proofs whilst his employer's young wife sat beside him reading aloud the text. During *Tiger Woman* (Elsa Evand) Blow became over-excited by the explicit text and his colleague's heavy breathing and shuffling and let numerous errors slip through. The book's publisher invoked the contract's penalty clause, exacted heavy compensation and Blow was sacked.

And don't trot out that hoary old "But I know nothing about publishing". You must have seen their standard WANTED in *The Guardian.*

Applicant will be a younger person although not necessarily in years. Additional advantage will be an interest in books.

Well you seemed quite young enough for me on that sandbar. And you *must* have read a book.

And Harpole, faced with a future ankle-deep in foldyards, rallied to the call, was installed in a converted out-house and, as Blow's stay overlapped two or three days, the two met, each taking an immediate liking to the other ("despite him wheezing worse than his blasted organ", G.H.). In fact, a memo by E.F. complains that, instead of pressing commercial investigation, Harpole spent too much time listening to Blow's lament that, now at long last, someone with a bit of education had turned up, he was more reluctant than ever to take himself off "just to mooch up and down with nobbut water to look at".

Whatever, in his salad days, may have been Blow's indiscretions, seemingly these had not disqualified him from the offices of Jordans Bank Churchwarden, Sunday-school Superintendent, Deanery Representative on the Diocesan Committee for the Care of Ecclesiastical Buildings and, more importantly, church organist. And he, cleverly spotting that Harpole was handicapped by a similarly disabling sense of public duty, urged upon him succession to these offices. Who demurred, protesting that an immediate elevation to such sought-after honours would foster local envy and hostility. Nor was he (Harpole) persuaded by Blow's assurance that, although volunteers had been invited in several successive parish-magazines, not a single candidate had stepped forward.

Then, when Harpole fell back upon a second line of defence by questioning how such prestigious appointments could possibly lie within Blow's gift, he was told that the parson left the running of everything to him, he being (but for a weekly sermon) the Vicar's sole channel of communication with his flock. And, unlikely as this must seem, it turned out to be true; for six days a week, the Revd J. G. Keech lurked within his gloomy parsonage, by day leaving it only to conduct an occasional funeral or to wander abroad along lanes and woodland paths on moonless nights.

Harpole surrendered.

The pair then crept through secret chambers of the organ so that Harpole might discover which keys stuck during humid summers, which in fogbound winters and which swells must never be pushed to their limit "for fear that the old girl might blow up and our Albert with her, trapped as he would be, in the organ-blower's loft."

And so, casting many a lingering look behind, Harold Blow was translated to Birchington-upon-Sea where, so it was said, whilst wandering its promenade during a dark night of the soul, he was ambushed by a Salvation Army commando patrol and set to learn the trombone.[*]

The inherited backlist of titles was pathetically meagre, restricted in range, outwardly drab and inwardly dull. Their saving grace was a local setting which recommended purchase by Barset folk as Christmas gifts for neighbours who had moved away and, like Blow, gazed fondly back at a lost paradise.

Barsetshire Highways & Byways
Graham Goulding

---

[*] Numerous literary memoirs acknowledge that swift and sadistic disposal of fictive characters goes some way towards salving ill-treatment of an author by publishers, agents, librarians and "neglect by the public at large".

It was Emma Foxberrow's belief that, save for the Book of Martyrs, Blow ("who by no manner of means is as dim as he looks"), in his younger days, had written the lot . . . punctuation courtesy the village school-mistress. She also swore that, to encourage beyond-Barset sales, he guiltily had invented authors whose names were vaguely reminiscent of those found in more exalted publishers' lists.

And, although Blow had left school aged 14, had neither read widely nor served his time with a professional publisher, this supposition may well have been true. The remarkable thing is that he had understood his best bet was to produce and offer for sale local items likely to be disregarded by London firms and more practised authors. As for his one-off re-publication of the 1563 edition of *Rerum Ecclesia Bestarum . . . Commentarii* (Book of Martyrs), he must have recognized that the gory woodcuts which had kept it in print for 400 years were even more relevant in our own bloodthirsty times.

In fact, Blow's single lapse of commercial judgment was

his organ pamphlet; here, personal enthusiasm had suborned economic good sense. (He was not the first publisher to stray and fall into that beguiling pit.)

*For Roman in Rome's quarrel spared neither gold nor state.
Then the great man helped the poor man and the poor man
loved the great.*

There was one further publication and this a splendidly profitable one – a hardback lavishly subsidised by Blow's landlord, Mr Arthur Fangfoss, a rich farmer living on the sugar-beet plain encompassing Steeple Sinderby, a neighbouring village. Some years earlier (and this is common knowledge) by an astonishing train of coincidence, the straggling community's football team, The Wanderers, had pulled off the most astounding recorded feat in the history of British sport: they won football's premier trophy, the FA Cup.

During that extraordinary single season, a substantial sum of money had accumulated from a share of away-gates. And, after a generous distribution to the players, this bonanza had been earmarked for (a) the refurbishment of a derelict chapel (once occupied by survivors of the Muggletonian Sect[*]) and (b) commissioning Joseph Gidner, a literary gent-of-passage unaccountably settled in the village, to write an official history of this *annus-mirabilis* and for Harold Blow to print and publish it. And for Blow this had been a godsend similar to the royal prerogative to produce King James's Authorized Version of the Holy Bible, profitably enjoyed for almost four centuries by the Oxford University Press.

This volume, its cover bound in crimson cloth and in gilt die-stamped Roman, entitled *The Glory Glory Days*, with reckless irrelevance was embellished by an engraving (also gilded) of a 14th Century Janus Cross. Its frontpiece (full

[*] Founded by Ludovick Muggleton. *c.*1667, a Northamptonshire tailor, who taught that God was small, bearded and dwelt in a large cube suspended six miles above Earth, where women immediately became men. He had a large female following. The last Muggletonian died in Chichester in 1943.

colour) displayed the Club Chairman, Mr Fangfoss, heavily moustached, seated in his heavily furnished parlour, wife and sister-in-law standing attentively behind him. Inset was a 8pp photographic folder – (i) The victorious XI with Mr F. centre front-row and, at its outskirts, a wild-looking man, (ii) Mr Fangfoss (courtesy of the *Barchester Messenger*) proposing a toast at the Sinderby Annual Bellringers' Sociable & Smoker, (iii) a composite picture of the Muggletonian Chapel before and after conversion, (iv) The back-room of The Black Bull, (v) Parson's Plow (a meadow), (vi) Dr & Mrs Kossuth, (vii) Mrs Thatcher alighting from a helicopter to be received by Mr Fangfoss in his office of Chairman of the Barset Constituency Conservative Party and (viii) The Royal Family by Gracious Consent of Her Majesty.

Time had eroded sales of this unusual document but Blow claimed that he had a steady and continuing call for it from elderly men and women who looked back to Mrs Thatcher's Britain as a latter-day Golden Age, when sturdy enterprise flourished, recidivists harshly put down, nationalized industry's idlers either rooted out or, after privatization, richly rewarded and made Chairmen. Certainly, it must be said that, during H. & F.'s incumbency, *The Glory Glory Days* remained a steady seller.

This book was a publisher's waking dream: The Fangfoss Trust sought no royalty payment. Nor did its author, he having settled for a handsome lump sum deposited in the Barchester Building Society (Chairman, Mr Fangfoss), its dividends augmenting his fitful income as a self-employed poet on piece-work in the Greeting Card Industry. In fact, the Trust's sole stipulation to Blow (to quote the Trust Deed) had been "to see to it we get a solid bit of literature up to and beyond what they can come up with down there in committee-ridden London."

That this publishing perk should be hung onto was

crucially important for the stripling enterprise and Blow, pausing during an organ tour, had earnestly counselled an early visit to Steeple Sinderby "to let 'em weigh you up, let 'em have a look at you, George. Rubbed up the wrong way, Arthur Fangfoss can be awkward, old man. Bloody awkward! As thu'll soon see for thissen."

Although the several hundred published Lives of the almost anonymous William Shakespeare disprove it, nowadays, even those authors like myself stirring about in remote and disregarded reaches of commercial history, depend utterly upon access to other people's piles of paper. And here I was fortunate, for not only had I known George Harpole and Emma Foxberrow (albeit in those last lingering years) but I had been given the "journals" (idiosyncratic diaries) which Harpole had left behind when, after Emma's death, he disappeared. ("Hetty dear, we both know you're one of life's scribblers and that, someday, you'll take a backward glance at the two of us. These notebooks may persuade you to give us benefit of your doubt.")

Harpole had been a ponderous recorder, forever dwelling upon irrelevance. And this is why, to give verisimilitude to this business-history, now and then I mean to condense and convert a few of his more longwinded entries from 1st to 3rd Person Singular . . . from reminiscence to narrative. As witness this account of his visit to Mr Fangfoss's lair.

*And from the ghastly entrance where the Bold Roman stood
Where, growling low, a fierce old bear waits amongst bones
and blood.*

The farmhouse, Towlers End, was a tall, three-storeyed, flat-fronted dwelling enveloped now by seemingly endless fields of oil-seed rape and sugar beet. Its sole embellishment was embedded above its front door – one half, sawn laterally, of that same medieval stone cross-head whose representation decorated the cover of *The Glory Glory Days*.

Skirting a couple of snarling dogs, he presented himself at the back door and to an overblown beauty doing the washing. No, no, he was told with a sly grin, she wasn't Mrs F. Mrs F. was her sister Annie (but who liked to be called Rowena) and she was upstairs scribbling. "Me, I'm nobbut Beatie." (Another grin.) And would he like to find his own way into the parlour, her boots being puddled-up?

There, seated uneasily on a chair's edge, several moments passed before he was aware of being gloomily observed from a dark corner by a large man. This person growled, "Don't bother telling me why you're here, young feller. You're that new chap who's taken over from Blow. And you've come about t'Book. Well, Mr Slingsby's gone off to that island and not likely to come back this year or t'next and t'Doctor 'll never come back fr' Budapest, so that leaves nobbut t'parson and what he doesn't leave to God, he leaves to me. And I leave t'Book business to Mr Gidner.* Now I'm off to see to mi beeasts."

He then left the room by a second door.

---

* Although sacked by a theological college, Gidner harboured no grudge against religion. He was described as a frail man wearing steel-rimmed spectacles. His mother was the only daughter of a South Dakota banker, Henry Farewell.

14

Harpole, now in some distress and apprehensive that he might well have put his foot in it and jeopardized valuable income, hurried out by way of Nobbut Beatie, thence to the village and its little museum. This was locked but, whilst loitering distractedly upon its doorstep, a dilapidated middle-aged man left a cottage and anxiously asked how he could help. This turned out to be Gidner ("the sort of chap who forever hangs about waiting for something disagreeable to happen to him") who urged Harpole to come over and "take a dish of tea".

Harpole's recollection is that they didn't immediately settle down to business but that he was given a small lecture on Gidner's method of blending and brewing tea . . . ("Brooke Bond's *English Breakfast* with a couple of pinches (no more) of Lapsang Soochang to give it a touch of je ne sais quoi . . . I never got out East. Did you?") before an unsought explanation of how it was that he was tenant and not owner of the cottage. And it was only after these tedious preliminaries that Harpole was told that there would be no fuss at all in transferring to him the book's printing and publishing.

MEMO HARPOLE (VERBATIM)

Told me "Furniture isn't mine either. It's Alex Slingsby's. Matter of fact you're sitting on the sofa where Diana passed away. No, that's not altogether true. What happened on the sofa's true enough. What I really meant was that a few oddments *are* mine. There's this picture (a heavily framed steel-engraving of *The Death of Nelson*). No, coming to think of it, that's not mine either: it's Dad's. It's all he came down with when he flitted from Bradford. ('It's your picture, isn't it Dad?')"

Until then I'd supposed we were alone. (Secret sharers seemed to abound in Sinderby.) A venerable old codger was concealed in a sagging horsehair armchair pushed deep into shadow by the fireplace.

(I examined the room's other corners; they were unoccupied.)

"Oh!" Gidner went on, "And I was forgetting the chair; he brought that down from Yorkshire, as well. ('Your chair, Dad, you brought that down as well, didn't you?') Yes, he says he brought that down as well. Mrs Sykes always told him it would come to him in her will. ('Didn't she Dad?') But then she got it into her head to move in with a married daughter, so he got it in advance. ('That's right, isn't it Dad. I've got that right, haven't I?') Yes, he says, That's right.

"So then it was Sheltered Accommodation up there or me taking him on down here. But he's very little bother and, for his age, he keeps himself pretty clean. He says *The Death of Nelson* brings back something that happened to him in South Dakota.[*] He's forever staring at it. Ever been there, Mr Harpole? South Dakota? No, I suppose not. Not many people have."

"Dad," he shouted, "This is Mr Harpole, Dad. You remember Mr Blow telling us about him. He's the new gentleman from Jordans Bank who's kindly taken over the Cup Final Book."

(Mr Gidner shuffled deeper into darkness.)

"Don't mind him, Mr Harpole; he can hear us all right. It's nothing to do with you. He's put out because Mr Blow's gone. Mr Blow understood him. They used to talk everlastingly about South Dakota even though Mr Blow hadn't been there. Dakota's where whatever happened to Dad happened. Granny once let drop he was just like the next chap till that one single year out there. But what do you suppose *The Death of Nelson* has to do with it?"

[*] George G. Gidner was one of the three witnesses of the climax of the so-called Battle of Pollocks Crossing.

16

Then Gidner and I went off to a rough meadow with a steep side-to-side slope. "Parson's Plow" he told me. "But it's not the parson's now; it's Mr Fangfoss's, like everything else round here. But this is where it happened. The Glory Glory Days! Here – on this bit of a field!" (He removed his cap.) "I expect I should have gone off like the rest did. But what happened that footballing winter and spring is about the only real thing ever to happen to me. I suppose that's why I've hung on here. Here, I'm somebody. Anywhere else I'd be nobody. I sometimes think that much the same sort of thing happened to Dad . . . out there in South Dakota. What do you think, Mr Harpole? Could it? Well, maybe not! Now I'll take you to the church; part of what happened, happened there also."

George Harpole, naturally, was (a) relieved to have this immediate confirmation of so valuable a continuing income and (b) much touched by Mr Gidner's reposal of personal confidences. So much so that, in the Black Bull's snug and a couple of hour's later, he insisted that H. & F. must publish his new friend's monograph, *Thos. Daddes, the Steeple Sinderby Peasant Poet, 1841-1884.* And, to boot, in a very limited, numbered, signed and no-expense-spared prestige edition.

It had been a most rewarding visit, he reported to Emma Foxberrow. But there had been that odd smell. No, not in Gidner's cottage. In the Black Bull.* It seemed to be coming up from beneath the snug's floor boards.

Nevertheless, beer and euphoria dispersed, he did not tell her of his already regretted promise ref. *Thos. Daddes* and was much relieved when, a couple of days later, a hand-

---

* Later taken over by the University of Ipswich for conversion into a Medieval Experience. Its foul smell was said to come from a Dutch seaman murdered for his pocket-watch. Later, this smell was chemically simulated.

delivered note from its author explained that, when he, Gidner, casually had mentioned the transaction to Mr Fangfoss, that panjandrum had declared that he, personally, would stump up for its publication, the Daddes* having been a very respectable family regular with their rent and, anyway as it happened, he (Fangfoss) had been looking about him for summat to give the village children to mark his fortieth year as Chairman of the Parochial School Governors and what better than a bit of poetry, "particularly as it was the rhyming sort and not likely to do nobody much harm".

* The Daddes family were hereditary vergers and thus i/c the church coke-fuelled stove mentioned in the Works of Thos. Daddes.

> *Let others sport in Sappho's Grove,*
> *Enough for me to tend this stove.*

and

> *Yet here I dwell, Stranger to Fame,*
> *But Tender of the Sacred Flame.*

PROCURATOR-GENERAL TO GEORGE BLOW, PRINTER.

Printed Works Copyright Act. Ed. VII 1908.

At your expense and within 7 (seven) days despatch to our Privileged Seats of Learning at the Universities of Oxford, Cambridge, Edinburgh, Aberystwyth and to Trinity College, Dublin, Republic of Ireland, at no costs to me or to the universities —

Pleasure Domes of Barset	*Jeffrey Amis*
The Elder & Alder Valleys Eating-Out Guide	*D. J. Simpson*
The Bag Sinderby Church Choir's Fatal Noctambulation together with The Miraculous Salvation of Thos. Leaf*	*Unattributed Author*
The Book of British Satyrs	*Geo. Foxe*

G.H. to E.F.

Can't really afford to *give* books away but we'd better be on the safe side?

E.F. to G.H.

The barefaced cheek! Blow's notepaper must have been headed "Geo. Blow, Philanthropist". If academic spongers want books let them cut off the wine tap to their High Tables and pay for them. Law! Whose Law? I bet that 1908 cabinet had nine Oxon and eight Cantab men, to the last man bumsucking for honorary D. Litts at no charge to themselves.

NO!

Harpole's Journal

Sent one each of all our books to Bruddersford Teacher-training college.

* One only of these 18th Century carol-singers survived drowning whilst being ferried across the Alder on Christmas Eve midnight, 1776. Thos. Leaf floated downstream upon the bass-fiddle strapped to his back. Next morning he was discovered beached at Higgleton (renamed Jordans Bank).

Forthwith uprose the Consul, uprose the Fathers all,
In haste they girded up their gowns and hied them to the
*   wall.*

Against common supposition − and an earlier aside in my book − there is manifest disadvantage when writers of commercial-histories know or have known prime-movers in their narrative. In my own case, it is true that I first knew Emma Foxberrow and George Harpole whilst I was no more than an 18 year-old Sixth-former and they already well into their seventies. Nevertheless, it is only fair to report that, before one died and the other disappeared, I spent three happy university vacs at Quince Tree Cottage up on Bredon Hill. So, however much I strive to present the pair objectively, personal recollection is bound to prejudice this prosaic account of the ebb and flow of their book business.

Continually and with much self-doubt I ask myself, Were these publishing innocents *my* Harpole and Miss Foxberrow only known to me 40 years on? Was this contented old lady, now Mrs Harpole, that attentive old gent, that same pair who, years before, had met in Tampling, parted in Sinji and met again at Jordans Bank? Who, for instance, could reconcile this Emma contentedly looking across the roofs of Mr Archer's barns westward into Wales with that earlier crazy voice talking from the darkness of Mrs Gilpin-Jones's[*] Birmingham boarding-house's Room One?

Have I let old acquaintances look too indulgently at their adventures in the Book Trade? Worryingly, it seems all too likely. For why else have I prefaced each episode with a line

[*] Rose Gilpin-Jones had employed (as companion-help) the author, Hetty Beauchamp, then an 18-year-old runaway Sixth-former. It was during this period that she first met Emma Foxberrow, and, later, George Harpole.

or two of George Harpole's favourite poem? To any skimmer it must seem that so idiosyncratic a gesture scarcely fits my remit − to serve up a cold collation of business history . . .

Yet . . . And yet it seems to me that Horatius on his bridge and the hesitant rise and dying fall of H. & F. have a not dissimilar epic air. And that this justifies an admonitory or encouraging word from Lord Macaulay's stirring tale of valour when Harpole himself faced similarly daunting odds. No? Well, let that be as it may . . .

During their earlier association at Tampling St Nicholas and in West Africa, although distressingly conscious of an educational and social inferiority, Harpole had a fair share of the see-saw . . . now and then even managing to urge good sense upon Emma Foxberrow. But now the boot was on the other foot and he knew it.

Although she had insisted upon Harpole's name joining her's on the firm's notepaper, because it was cash from a family trust which had bought out Blow, not unreasonably the direction of the fledgling firm was her's. Much later, Edwin Shutlanger (of whom, more later) slily recalled being told, "It was her money, you know. Jolly good of her to call us H. & F., but let's face it, I was dogsbody. Well, let's say I was under-dog. But, coming to think about it, I suppose I'd always been someone's doormat and, frankly, I really didn't mind being Emma's assistant instead of her headmaster. Perhaps I should look up a psychiatrist . . ."

But now the immediate need was an expansion of Blow's list and, persuaded by compelling arguments of haste, reduced costs and finding something for Blow Junior to set about printing and for Harpole to sell, Emma proposed a cheap edition of those English poets largely unread by their countrymen but still esteemed by examination boards − John Keats, Percy Shelley and so on.* These would be a slim

* John Donne was the best-seller. Those too few early poems celebrating

32pp and (i) in the main geared to the simple needs of comprehensive schools yet (ii) with an eye on the gift-trade. Their format would be half-hardback (8-sheet card), their front cover invitingly decorated by a monochrome portrait and (a gesture towards academic respectability) a fragment of the poet's handwriting scrawled across the outer back-cover. And each volume would be illustrated lavishly "to cut down typographical charges and to give slow-readers a break".

Initially, Harpole complained that 32 pages was too meagre fare but, when his partner sardonically enquired when he, personally, had last waded through *Paradise Lost, In Memoriam* or *The Faerie Queen,* he neither pressed his cause nor contested her naive insistence that would-be purchasers, turning up a first page, must discover something "familiar to the average favourite aunt". Thus, Wordsworth opened his innings with "I wandered lonely as a cloud", William Blake with "And did those feet", Cowper — "John Gilpin was a citizen . . ." and W. B. Yeates emerged from copyright announcing that he would arise now and go to Innisfree.

"Take old Bob Browning" Miss F. pontificated. "Push *Karshish, An Epistle* under a browser's nose and he'll dig no deeper than its title. Whereas confront him with *The Pied Piper of Hamelin* and there's short odds it will bring some dear old school-ma'am's dramatic rendering of the same to mind when he was a nipper. And you've sold the book."

"And anyway" she added menacingly, "It will give that idler Albert Blow a job. And, while he's on the agenda, order him to remove those calendar-girl cut-outs he's undraped on the printshop wall. Are all printer's machine-operators sex-crazed? Apart from keeping his mini-mind from what's rolling off his press, they are an affront to his mother."

---

sexual rather than holy fervour were popular with younger readers who rebutted parental protest by asserting that the author was a Canon of St Paul's Cathedral and thus OK.

The idea turned out to be a sound move. Several of the nation's slow-selling poets, Meredith, Flecker, Robert Bridges and Ben Jonson who, outliving their shelf-life in publishers' warehouses, had been sentenced (without appeal) to long spells of O/P, still had devotees enough to make a modest revival worthwhile. So here H. & F. had a clear field and it was not unusual for Blackwell of Oxford, who catered for a worldwide circuit, to stoop and scatter in their direction single-orders from exiles hanging on in lost pockets of Empire.

Nevertheless the future was predictable – either a successful sales effort by the ill-equipped Harpole* or collapse when Emma Foxberrow's back-up money no longer could cover Albert Blow's wages, typography charges, plate-making, paper costs and household expenses. For, even with the projected poets, their list could be only a stop-gap until, somehow, they could generate publications likely to attract attention from literary editors and their reviewers and, then, booksellers' orders. But what hope of such publishable mss landing on Jordans Bank! Their slender resources would never attract authors with an established book-buying following, nor was it likely that any agent holding a promising book would offer this to H. & F. whilst even the faintest chance of placing it with an established London publisher remained.

Thus, off their own bat, they would need to find competent but unpublished writers with attractive ideas or, at very least, technically competent authors crazed to get into print who, at barely survival rates, could be set to work at an in-house project and then put up with cold-blooded belittling editing.

As ever, chance now took a hand.

---

* Harpole later complained that his sole instruction was from a Birmingham rep, Fred Pendleberry, who told him there was no point in visiting shops displaying small postcards in their windows saying BOOKS FOR SALE. These, he was told, sold only pornography in bogus jackets, eg, *Queen Victoria's Balmoral Diaries.*

Their van will be upon us before the bridge goes down;
And if they once may win the bridge, what hope to save the
town?
Then up spake brave Horatius, the Captain of the Gate . . .

It must have been about this critical time that a shadowy half-forgotten figure from his past wrote to George Harpole. This was Edwin Shutlanger, MA (Oxon), sometime Headmaster of Tampling Grammar School, who Harpole recalled as an overweight, shambling chap (egg on waistcoat, booze on breath), bringing to mind portraits of Ford Madox Hueffer, the celebrated Georgian novelist.

> Well, old chap, you will be as astonished to hear from me as I was of you when I ran into good old Harold Blow at the Diocesan Synod and was told you were back in dear old Barset. Long ago, Blow put to rights my church coke-burning stove at Oxgodby when (briefly) I was incumbent there. And, en-passant, I may say he tremendously impressed me; he *talked* machines into doing their duty. Quite remarkable! That damned stove had beaten every so-called expert in Yorkshire. Old Mossop told me it had been on their PCC's agenda even in his grandad's time. But Blow just sits himself down on a chair and *looks* at it. In fact, I've long had it in mind to write a little memoir. . . . But that's neither here nor there.
>
> As you see, I'm back in Tampling. I won't go on about it but when Mimi came home from her frolic with that Big Sixth-former . . . oh well, I suppose I might as well tell you the whole sorry story; if I don't, someone else will. And, after all, you were in at the start . . . when Mimi ran off, I mean.
>
> I expect you heard I sent in my papers. Just couldn't stand the sight of lads (remembering that scoundrel Smith) and, despite everything, I was missing her badly.

I'll admit to giving at least half-a-dozen others a run-out. (Well, hang it all, I'm not so broken-down as I may look and the years were leaking away.) But they were as nothing to Mimi. Nothing! But you weren't born yesterday, Harpole; I expect you know what I mean, eh?

So, to take my mind off her and it, I signed on at a C of E seven day meditative retreat. (No talking, arctic bed-rooms and an everlasting smell of overboiled cabbages.) That didn't cool me off – the less I talk, the more I think. So I joined-up fulltime with an Anglican Brotherhood and they posted me to one of their monasteries up on the Yorkshire moors and, in no time at all, the east wind and none of their doors fitting put me to rights. (Though *they* claimed it was low living and high thinking.) Anyway, they turned me out to train as a parson.

As a matter of fact, I wasn't half bad at it: the only complaint that ever came to my ears was I tended to be a bit on the gloomy side when marrying folk. But back to Mimi . . . now that I've started, I might as well finish. Well, in the end, she repented, the business coming to a head at Oxgodby, significantly enough, the Fourth Sunday after Trinity, at evensong. (You *are* C of E, Harpole?)

I'd just launched out into "Dearly beloved brethren, the Scriptures moveth us in sundry places to acknow-ledge our manifold sins and wickednesses . . ." (But you know the rest of that rigmarole as well as I do. Or are you a Plymouth Brother? You always struck me as having a hangdog look about you.)

Well, as I was saying, I'd got about halfway when it dawned on me some odd goings-on were brewing down in the shadows at the back-end of the nave. It looked to me as if old Colonel Hebron, the People's Warden and Mossop (the verger) were making no headway at all pushing someone out who was hellbent on getting in. (And all this argy-bargy was going on in dead silence as

well as dead earnest. Of course, Harpole, being a church-
man yourself, you'll understand that, but for me and the
choir, not a soul could spot what was happening.)

But when I lost the thread of what I was supposed to be
droning (being fascinated by the other performance) I
must have come to a full-stop because the congregation
became uneasy, first twisting their necks and then the
rest of their bodies. All the same, except for the back
pews, like me they couldn't make out what was going on
till the trouble-maker wheeled the scrum, dummied past
the Colonel and cleverly side-stepped Mossop's admittedly high-tackle.

And, to my utter amazement, it was Mimi. Making her
way up the middle aisle. And in a sack.

In a sack! But not hopping like on a sports day. No, the
sack was wrong way up. The poor thing had cut a hole in
its bottom for her head to go through and a couple more
holes for her arms and, as far as I could see, that's all she
had on. Just the sack! Sackcloth! Not a stitch! Not even
shoes! And, by the way, it wasn't a coal sack; it had on it
ALLINSON'S STONEGROUND WHOLEMEAL FLOUR
MILLED IN CASTLEFORD. (Queer how useless detail
lodges in one's memory, isn't it Harpole?)

Anyway, when she got to the front, she stood below
my pulpit with her head bowed. Penitentially – because
she turned up her eyes and muttered *Peccavi*. (You see
the clever little body had remembered I'd picked up the
odd Latin tag when I was up at Oxford.) But you'd never
guess what got me down. I expect you're thinking,
"Unholy glares from the front pews". Wrong! It was her
bare little feet. But what really hit me for six was that
she'd sprinkled ashes on her head and it must have been
drizzling outside because the black was running down
her face. (And I expect you remember what an absolutely super-blonde Mimi is.)

Naturally, everything had come to halt. Not a sound!

26

"Go on – play something" I muttered to the organist. "Anything!" But the stupid creature was as dumbstruck as the rest of them. Then Old Mossop pulled himself together and switched to automatic-pilot. And began, *"We have done those things we ought not to have done and left undone those things we ought to have done . . ."* which was enough to start the rest of them braying. Pretty smart of the poor old dodderer when you come to think of it! Only goes to show what an advantage lads had in the old days, leaving their elementary-schools before book-learning dimmed their wits. Mind you, I don't think for a minute he saw how apt it was. (Not that you could ever tell with Mossop. But, if he did, in the circs it was a bit near the bone, eh Harpole?)

Then I left them to get on with it as best they could, bustled the poor little creature into the vestry, bundled her into a choirman's cassock and carried her off in my arms through the priest's door, across the graveyard and home. Then, when I'd given her a hot foam bath and a shampoo, I put her to bed. And all this time she kept a stiff upper-lip. Not a whimper! Well Harpole, you don't need to be told – Mimi always had spunk.

I'm not going to make out I wasn't upset. Who wouldn't be? But *exhilarated* if that makes any sort of sense. No?

And next day I sent in my papers again and the Bishop did the decent thing – let us stay on in the Vicarage, doing no more than hint that, until he could draft in the next man, he'd rather we didn't go out till after dark.

Then I took up headmastering again. And that's another story.

Now Harpole, I felt it no more than right for you to know what I've been through, because of what I'm really writing to you about. It's this. Blow told me you're doing a bit of book-publishing and, as I'd like to get into print

27

(to take my mind off things), I want to put a little idea to you . . .

This bizarre letter was harbinger of the first of those two extraordinary books which were to bring the tiny enterprise's name to the public's attention and for which, perhaps, the Book Trade best remembers it, For it heralded *The Story for the English* which, brief though it was, Shutlanger had been working at for at least a couple of years.

It was an unusual book, difficult to fit into cataloguese. It has been described as a latter-day appendix to the Four Gospels,* as an eccentric commentary upon them, as a satirical sermon. . . . And such classifications were not wide of the mark because, basically, it was a crude amalgum of those testamental incidents which Shutlanger supposed relevant to late 20th Century England. For instance, it is significant that he suppressed mention of what he must have considered starlight magic – a virgin birth, instant alcoholic fermentation, water-walking and sundry feats of levitation.

My personal difficulty at an exact classification was shared by those librarians who reluctantly felt it a public duty to order a copy: it was one of those bothersome books which mess up the fîche. Over the years, I have come across it lodged under SOCIOLOGY, THEOLOGY, ANTHRO-POLOGY and (once) as JUVENILE FICTION. Others hid it in remote corners amongst OUTDATED STOCK. And at one library in North Wales and everywhere in Ulster, loan was discouraged by quarantining it in basement cupboards ONLY TO BE UNLOCKED IN THE PRESENCE OF TWO SENIOR STAFF.

The principal figure in Shutlanger's concoction was a Mr Thisman who, inexplicably taking early retirement from employment as a building-site carpenter, appears out of the blue

---

* One tabloid unkindly named it *The Gospel according to Edwin.*

amongst the pit drainage lakes of the South Yorkshire Coal-fields from where, recruiting a dozen similar working-class disruptives, he sets off on an evangelical walkabout. They make their haphazard way through an England overtly governed by monarch and parliament but, like some banana republic, covertly managed off-stage by a massive United States Military presence – that manic nation having nomi-nated Britain as its outer bulwark against a nightmare Communist/Muslim aggressor.

Perhaps "evangelical" is misleading, bringing to mind a Billy Graham bang n' bash electronic Mission. Nothing could have been less alike. Thisman simply wanders down to Birmingham, up to Sheffield, down to Brighton. There is no shilly-shallying. He simply preaches no hope for a heaven hereafter but earnestly urges the English to move heaven on earth.

Police Special Branch, MI5, the CIA, report his inflam-matory harangues to an irritated Establishment and an affronted American High Command. But, rather than publi-cising him by suppression, word is put about by a lickspittle Press that he is a layabout nutter. In fact, all might have been well, had Thisman stayed clear of London. But to London he goes and Shutlanger's final pages (quite moving, as a matter of fact) find his explosive pronunciamentos exciting massive street demos by a wide social range of citizens demanding an instant Kingdom of Heaven (but retaining the Royal Family).*

Standard palliatives are offered by Government – infla-tionary pay-deals, subsidised housing, students and Lloyds-names' debt cancellations, mortgage interest rates of $2\frac{1}{2}\%$. And promises of endless committees of endless enquiry. But

---

* A Mass Observation Survey reported divergent definitions of Heaven-upon-Earth ranging from year-long public holidays to compulsory daily churchgoing.

multiplying mobs still howled for Heaven Here and Now.

So, during a Kensington Garden night sleep-in, Thisman is quietly picked up, arraigned before a military tribunal and given Life. Documentary evidence of his trial and sentence disappear: he becomes a non-person. And survives only as a vague and garbled memory.

There have been other interpretations of *The Story* but mine, I believe, is a fair summary of Shutlanger's plot.

Deny it, as often he did, Shutlanger's tale naggingly brings to mind another such fatal journey and its bitter end: time after time one hears an uneasy echo of another story. And its suggestion of a Second Coming? Well, such likelihoods seem always to have had an attraction for the English – Arthur, Once and Future King, Drake and his Drum of Salvation, a drowned yet delivered Field Marshal Kitchener. These are part and parcel of our island myth. As George Herbert (admittedly a Welshman) puts it,

> Ah, what time wilt thou come?
> When shall that cry,
> "The Bridegroom cometh",
> Fill the sky?

And there are other disturbing Testamental similarities.

Like the once familiar four gospels, the telling of Shutlanger's *Story* is told as simply as a child's bedtime tale, as impersonally, as a matter of *fact*. Like them, the narrative is bare of scenic description, there is no conjecture, no flim-flam, no exploration of its characters' motives, elaboration of their physical looks, their personal traits.

And, finally, like the gospels, there is that one, that single too human cry from the heart ("My God, why hast thou forsaken me?") For Jack, Thisman's closest friend, hangs fearfully around the top security jail where he believes Authority has hidden his mate. And one night out there, beyond the floodlights and across the enveloping wasteland,

he hears a lamentable cry, "Heaven is all about us. It is Here."
Answered by "Not in Pottersfield it ain't, squire". And a
single shot.

Because of subsequent events, I believe that George
Harpole's later assertion that *The Story* did not go through on
the nod was true. He claimed that he read and re-read the
manuscript and his opinion was that it amounted to no more
than a pretentious fancy. With hindsight, one charitably
must suppose that his critical faculty was muffled by its
author's impressive curriculum-vitae – Oxford scholar,
Anglican brother, parish priest. And, finally, any persisting
misgivings probably were stifled by Shutlanger's waiving of
claim to royalty payment. ("My sole expectation, old man, is
that my trifling confection may be relished by a few (alas)
discriminating palates.") Well, well!

In her turn, it is undisputed that Emma Foxberrow *did*
know that the book was of a theological nature but,
supposing that, probably, it was a mothballed thesis from
Shutlanger's aborted campaign for ecclesiastical preferment,
didn't read it. And one must admit that her decision was
cold-bloodedly rational. A book was needed. Shutlanger had
a book. It was a theological book. Theology, like cricket,
cooking and the railways, had a reliable core of book-buyers.
Her partner, Harpole, who played cricket, liked his fodder
and had hoped to be an engine-driver, was a steady
churchgoer. Harpole had told her they should publish. QED.

And thus, caution going by default, *The Story for the
English* was dumped upon dull necessity's conveyor-belt.
Albert Blow was told to print an edition of 500 copies on the
cheapest paper and to see to it that it was perfect-bound* in

---

* "Perfect bound" does not mean "perfectly bound". Usually it describes a
book in which cover and pages have been stuck together under pressure.
Nor does a page of type which has been "justified" have a spiritual
connotation.

8-sheet card so that it might be described to booksellers as "almost hardback", yet retailed for £4.99. Its cover was to be Bible-black, title and author (heavily credited with MA Oxon, LlB) displayed in scarlet, supported by a couple of unattributed banners lifted with breathtaking irrelevance from other publishers' *Booktrader* advertisements,

BIZARRE! TOTALLY ORIGINAL!
A LATTER DAY CANTERBURY TALE!
THIS CHILLING CRESCENDO OF NARRATIVE POWER!

Blow's proposal that by working Sunday at treble-rates he could deliver within three weeks was repulsed, Harpole asserting that, since its author was an ex-clergyman, such a breach of the Fourth Commandment would be unforgivable. And, unexpectedly, Albert accepted this. ("You never can tell with God these days. . . .") But then, resuming his normal bloody-mindedness, he went on to complain of Shutlanger's daily authorial poppings-in to ask, "How's ma baby doin' Bert?"

And how man die better than by facing fearful odds
For the ashes of his fathers and the temples of his gods?

Meanwhile George Harpole's sales forays had turned out to be moderately successful and, in schools, particularly so. Here, of course, he was on familiar ground, making his sales approach matey by cleverly feeding flattering leads likely to encourage headteachers into self-congratulation and over-ordering. Providing he was given a minimum order for 25 copies of any of the standard poets, he offered a discount of 40% on their retail price of 75 pence. This emboldened some EngLit teachers to put the poets on their syllabi and then to sell them to their pupils at full price, thus not only making modest contributions to their domestic economies but side-stepping bruising encounters with chemistry-teachers become headmasters dedicated to the starvation of the humanities.

But selling books to booksellers was a different kettle of fish and initial sales expeditions left him shaken. For he discovered the reversal of roles from buyer to seller startlingly diminished his standing. Even the shops them-selves presented a disheartening face. As a purchaser, he had rejoiced in heavily book-laden shelves; as a seller, such a sight appalled him. How, he lamented, How could any sensible merchant be persuaded to augment what he plainly had more than enough of?

It says much for the nature of the man that, heart in boots, time after time he presented himself at the breach. As I write this and recalling that honourable plodder, I find an elabora-tion of his travail too distressing. This diary summary of a single day on the road tells all. (Town names are omitted to avoid offence.)

TOWN A. Bought mint humbugs before plonking display-case on counter. Chap rocked on heels. Pulled himself together. Muttered he sold only confectionery and tobacco and the sundays. Had never cared much for books – Weren't books best left standing as trees? Had heard that some books could change your life and he was happy as he was. And didn't the IRA put bombs in hollowed-out books? The only good he'd heard of about books was if you happened to have one in your breast-pocket when struck by a bullet. Apart from that, what earthly use had books? Books couldn't be sucked, chewed or smoked. Asked if I stocked scented-soap. Said at a pinch he might subscribe a small carton of scented-soap. You could always bath yourself with soap. Never heard of anyone immersing himself in a book. Also his part-time shop lady was into Green Thinking and had warned him some books left a dangerous residue.

Couldn't find words to counter this. Coming to think about it, except for a pile to stand on to get at a top shelf, there isn't much can be done with a book except read it. Stared hopelessly at each other. Chap's nerve broke first. Said OK, OK, he'd take a couple of John Miltons. Wasn't he the chap who dwelt in a graveyard? Recollected something about a graveyard in Mr Kirby's English class. Wasn't there some cows in it? Mr Kirby had told them the poetical name for cows was "lowing herd", so he'd have one Milton for himself to keep his mind off being sucked out if a window smashed on his next package-holiday flight, also one for his sister-in-law. Brother had told him a bit of poetry livened her up last thing at night, "Lucy's his second" he told me. Winked. Paid cash from till. Winked again.*

TOWN B. Knew was in for hard time when saw placard on

---

* Much later, this Mr Pledger was appointed Littlewood Professor of Everyday Literature at Liverpool and claimed that his taste for books was aroused in conversation with a wandering rep whose name he had forgotten but who had tried to sell him some scented-soap.

big box of Jeffrey Archer's — EAT YOUR DINNER ELSE-
WHERE. THIS IS A DUMPBIN NOT A DUSTBIN. Man refused
to look at wares. Nudged me doorward. Pityingly explained
his meagre profits diminished merely by taking a book from
customer's hand, wrapping book for customer, accepting
payment for book from customer, giving customer change
for book, handing book back to customer. Declared John
Milton would lose him 5p each time he sold one. Laughed
scornfully, "Milton! Who reads dreary old Milton these days!
You couldn't even sell me a Milton *bookmark.*" Customers
looked hostiley at me. Slunk out.

But one lady whispered, "That man is an oaf. His last shop
was a fish-and-chipper. The sooner Mr Waterstone moves in
on him the better. You can take my solemn word for it, JM
had him in his sights when he penned,

"The hungry sheep looked up and were not fed."

But for evolutionary throwbacks like him (not Mr Waterstone), folk like you and me still would be on holiday in the
Garden of Eden."

However, when I proffered a Milton at full trade discount,
she hurried away.

TOWN C. Fruitlessly retreating from gifte shoppe slipped
on olde stone floore. Brought down couple of cast-iron gilt
and cream milkmaidens. Both cracked, clattered apart.
Proprietor hastened to my aid till saw milkmaids. Lamented,
"Now look what you've done to these ornamental door-
stoppers. Nine quidsworth gone for a burton! Look here,
both in the trade, squire. Charge you what they cost me."
(Rubbed ear, sure sign of approaching lie.) "Seven quid! OK
squire?"

Picked myself up. Protested hadn't wanted to fall on his
floor. Said his flags slippy and me in leather-soled shoes. Told
him was not a squire. Hopefully twitched up trouser-leg.

Small bubble of blood pulled itself together and crept down kneecap. Both gazed mournfully at it. Moaned I'd need his insurer's address. Tetanus . . . gangrene . . . lifetime in wheelchair . . . never can tell with all this pollution about . . .

"OK, OK," man said, "Forget it." Then gave me one plaster bookend bust of William Shakespeare. "Have to stock 'em" he told me savagely, "Blasted local author!"

TOWN D. (Stotfield Magna). Proprietor Mrs Fazackerly. Bright-eyed knowing-looking Welshwoman. Also very well built. Said she would take a half-dozen *Foxe's Book of British Satyrs*. When I pointed out that they were *Martyrs,* she said she'd still have them. Remarked on limp. Asked me into her back-parlour. Big gold harp in corner. Knelt and dressed wound. Noted Mrs F. genuine undyed blonde. Very rare these days of Glowsheen with everything. Told me used to be librarian but didn't let on to boy-friends. Told them she had no GCEs and worked in Woolworths. Got more dates that way.

Invited Mrs Fazackerly to supper at The Bull. She had spare-rib with crocquets. I had roast-duckling. Excellent value for money. Told her experiences grave and gay in Sinji. Mrs F. commented "I bet you went down well with those big and beautiful black ladies, Mr Harpole. Am very fond of cricket myself. Particularly that Gower. And your next visit the meal will be on me. Also send me a couple of dozen more *Satyrs.*" Also promised to give me a tune on her harp.

Mrs Fazackerly is not just a bookseller. She is a book-person. Said her favourite author was Mrs Byatt and often had a go at her. Said any chapter of Mrs Byatt's did her good like going for a brisk walk in the country. Also said she (Mrs F.) looked on books, even Good Hotel Guides, as cultural icons. Just to *sell* a book was prestigious.

Mrs Fazackerly also told me, "In the winter, I start off my day by stroking one of the books. One of Mr Holroyd's good solid biographies is best. Biographies of folk not overlong dead like to be stroked. And I feel sort-of-something going up my arm as if his biographee was getting into my bloodstream and then into my head. Also explained each book has its own aura: even remaindered Knitting Patterns were handy for putting wet glasses on.

Mrs Fazackerly (Avona) also is a wag. Quipped, "You should publish a *Good Eating-out Guide to Bookshops.* And give stars for dark corners where the bank-clerks and secretaries can eat their sandwiches undisturbed. And double stars for doubly-dark corners for doing other things in. ("Well, as I always say, such as you Mr Harpole and me, are young only the once.") Nudged me. Did not mention a Mr Fazackerly. Nor did I Emma Foxberrow.

Give and take, felt my day well spent.

And underneath is writ in letters all of gold
How valiantly he kept the bridge in the brave days of old.

A contemporary though curtailed account of H. & F.'s publishing activities (*TLS vol. ccclv*) names Emma Foxberrow as prime-mover in building the firm's list. (Its author does not reveal her/his sources.) But is this true? In fact, there is well-documented evidence that the most significant titles sprang from George Harpole's much earlier acquaintance with their authors. Nothing supports this more significantly than the manner in which the second and third books were commissioned.

Harpole quickly had learnt that, in the trade, Mondays unkindly were substituted as the weekly break for shop assistants. On that hopeless day, the proprietor or manager irritably took over the till and received wandering reps with a chilliness verging upon incivility. So, sensibly, Harpole devoted the beginnings of each week to a round of visits to Barset schools, seeking to persuade their heads to stock library copies of inherited Blow local-histories. And thus 9.15, on one such morning, found him reconnoitering the village of Sawpits, a dispirited straggle of cheap brick, halfway between Tampling St Nicholas and Barchester.

From rough notes in his diary I have fleshed out what befell him.

Outside the school a picket of two determined women had a crude banner, SAWPITS SCHOOL FOR SAWPITS KIDS, whilst a heavier pair leant on the doors of a this year's registration Rover, preventing its occupants from alighting. An elderly lady at her garden's gate explained to Harpole that, "it was just another couple of money-bags from

Barchester trying to wheedle their kiddies in and squeeze our kiddies out of our school. Then, drawing my attention to a Mercedes-Benz tucked into a nearby front garden she said, "As well as this council-house (not that they ever sleep in it), I have heard tell how these new neighbours of mine have a big spot with peacocks out in the country. But, as our Sawpits is the only school round here, free or paid-for, where there is any solid old-fashioned education to be got these days, having this address puts their Caroline, Giles and Miles into our catchment area.

This extraordinary information stirred Harpole's latent professional curiosity, for the prospect before him was un-promising – a crumbling playground, earth-closets masked by a coke heap, a fortresslike facade grudgingly lit by Gothick window-slits. So, establishing identity as a non-parent, he penetrated a jungle of cast-iron clothes pegs to discover this notice,

THE HEADMISTRESS MAY BE FOUND
IN HER SCHOOLROOM – TEACHING.

Foraging onward, to his amazement, he came upon a member of his sometime Tampling staff, Miss Grace Tollemache, standing by a Victorian counting-house desk and vigorously conducting an immense class singing its multiplication tables. When these triumphantly had confirmed that thirteen thirteens were 169, she turned and, immediately recognizing her former headmaster, ex-claimed, "Children, here is that Mr Harpole of whom many's the time I have told you. For a while, he and I will be engaged in conversation. Begin where you left off committing to memory *How Brave Horatius Kept the Bridge*. And those who already have it by heart, get on with the nets you are knotting. ("It's to condition them for the deadly mono-tonous and laborious tasks that await the poor little souls in later life" she whispered. "Better for them to learn early than late what the years have in store. And their dads always can find use for a net . . . catching fishes on Sundays, keeping blackbirds off the rasps and, the better-off ones, for driving golf balls into.")

This encounter was so unexpected that George Harpole, never a one for extemporization, launched himself into his concocted sales-patter whilst spreading a sample of his wares across Miss Tollemache's desk. She, on the other hand, was regarding him with utmost attention.

"I had heard on the grapevine that you were back in the County" she interrupted. "But why haven't you taken on some teaching? I suppose you still are stuck on that Emma Foxberrow and she put you off it down there in Africa. You would be put out at the tittle-tattle that went the rounds at NUT meetings – that you had been made a tribal chieftain with four or was it 40 wives, that you were chained to a dungeon floor, that you had discovered King Solomon's gold mines. . . . And that is to mention only three milder items from your biography."

"But many's the time I have stood up for you. 'I owe everything to Mr Harpole' I tell traducers. 'But for him I still should be everlastingly teaching those Backwards that old phoney Chadband stuck me with because I wasn't college-trained and hadn't a certificate or a degree like the rest of you.' "

"I expect nobody told you I was a Head myself these days. Though you might as well know *They* only gave me the job because no-one else applied for it. I mean to say – Sawpits! Who would? You must have seen what a dump it is. I did write to let you know but I suppose Africa's a big place and the letter didn't find you. Well, now, here I am, top of the tree. Top of this tree anyway!"

(The class worked on in industrious silence. Eye-lashes

fluttered, lips moved soundlessly, little fingers knotted nets.)

"I run things along what I call the Harpole Method" she went on. "And if you don't know what that is, who does? The children like it, their parents like it and I like it. Only those new inspectors *They* send to spy on me don't like it. *Them!*

"And Mr Harpole, do stop calling me 'Miss'. I am a 'Mrs' nowadays. That also was in the letter which didn't find you."

She did not elaborate. Merely looked knowingly at him.

Although flabbergasted by this news, Harpole did not probe it. And, changing tack, he asked if she kept in touch with any of their former colleagues – Mrs Grindle-Jones, the Abominable Croser or James Alfred ("One-of-the-Old-School") Pintle.

"Pintle!" she exclaimed, "Pintle!"

And went off into sardonic laughter. (The children worked steadily on.)

"Pintle! . . . Reader, I married him."

Having always assumed that Miss Tollemache had earmarked a contented lifetime free of wedded hazard, Harpole was staggered. As for Pintle marrying, imagination reeled.

Regrettably she read his thoughts.

"Well, neither of us were growing younger" she continued defiantly, "and, to tell you the truth, I felt sorry for the old boy. And – cards on the table – also for myself. Mr H., what I am trying to tell you is that there we were, me with one foot in the grave and Pintle already in up to his knees . . . and neither him nor me knowing the pains and pleasures of love."

"What brought us to the brink was his landlady selling-up in that crazy house-price boom and going off to live with a daughter in Brum, leaving Pintle high and dry. I came across him buying a rope in that ironmongers Rachel Billitt serves in on a Saturday. (Don't tell me you've forgotten her dad, that gorilla, Billitt!) And Pintle looked in more than a pickle. His shirt collar was frayed and there was egg yolk on his waist-coat, all of which must distress you, recalling how spruce he used to keep himself. But the real giveaway was his little moustache. You know how he kept it clipped. (Croser used to enquire where he bought his mini-lawnmower.) Well, now it was looking like an Old English Sheepdog.

And, if this wasn't bad enough, he went on and on about his troubles and how he would end up in that Home down by the Sewerage. In fact, I could see it only needed a word in the wrong place to set him off crying. Fancy! Pintle weeping! So, without giving it a second thought, I said, 'Look here, Pintle, you can move in with me. Tampling being what it is, a sump of backbiters, for the look of things we'll go through some sort of marriage hooha. And then you can settle yourself into the backbedroom: at the moment, like Eden, there's only apples in it. And now Rachel here will give you your money back, as you won't need that rope for tying up your travelling trunk. Or was it for something else?' "

"And that was what we did. And, as you'll see, he's got his moustache back to where it was and better. Oh, he's no bother at all. Even though it wasn't love that brought us to it, all's turned out as I knew it would. He's ever so useful about the house; he'll do the weekly supermarket shop and the hoovering and won't let me lay a finger on the washing-machine now he's go the better of it. But then, you'll remember how it was with him; everything had to be just-so with James Albert. You should see his ironing; it is a work of art so I let him do the lot but for my undies. Well not them, naturally! And now he's had a few cookbooks out of the library, he's a better hand at the pot than me. And he'll even do the Christmas cards."

She must have spotted a twinge of envy because she went

on, "You should give it a try yourself, Mr H. Married life, I mean! I've always said the right woman would be the making of you. Well, perhaps I ought to say, Put the finishing touches on."

"He's a very lucky man to have caught you . . . Mrs Pintle," Harpole said. "A very lucky man!"

"Well, when I look around at the mess some folk make of things, I suppose you're not far out" she replied, doing a mock bow. "But, to be fair, I give him ten-out-of-ten too. He's very gentlemanly and never oversteps the mark. I have never seen him in his nightshirt, let alone without it."

She paused, looking significantly at Harpole. "But he misses his teaching. Not the children. Pintle never cared over much for children: he'd have been just as happy teaching a class of waxworks. So, nowadays, it's his book that keeps him going."

"His book!" Harpole exclaimed. "Why, he once told me that he didn't read books. He gave them up with exams."

"Not his reading-book. His *writing*-book. *His* book! You must remember his book – he tells everyone that it was you got him going on it.

"It goes back to that time when the two of you had a set-to because you wouldn't punish that Welsh lad, the gas-manager's son, for arguing with Pintle about people being fed up with coal fires and wanting gas-central heating. It blew up over an arith problem about the mistress (A) sending her housemaid (B) downstairs to fetch scuttles of coal until the cellar (C) was empty and that Welsh lad telling Pintle nobody on the new estates had a cellar (C) nor a housemaid (B) and wanted his/her house ready warmed up with the gas when she/he (A) got back from work. And you told him the boy was right to stick to his guns and that things had moved on since Pintle was a lad in Bayswater.

He told me you upset him into getting no sleep that night.

43

But, next morning, you'd apologized and said Pintle ought to write up his stories about those little problem-arith chaps, A, B, C and and that awful demolition fellow X – Pintle's maths method the Maharajah had thought so highly of when Pintle was out in India tutoring his wives (the Maharajah's wives). The Prince's favourite was A and B trying to fill their bath with X sneaking in all the time and pulling out the plug.

Well, ever since, he's been doing just what you told him to do – writing that book. And, when he can't find any housework to get on with, out it comes from its drawer and he polishes it up.

Of course, we both know it's not the maths *They* (the experts) say we must teach these days, *They* say that A, B, C and that X, such as you and me learnt our maths from, are dead as dodos. (She repeated *They* with venom.) Well, we have an opinion on experts, don't we, Mr H?

"Now I know book-publishing isn't cheap" she went on. "But if you would like a look at Pintle's and, if you find it up to scratch and, if you think there is a call for it from good old-fashioned backward-looking schools *They* haven't managed to ferret out and shut . . . well, then the pair of us would both have fingers in the printer's pie. (I expect you've not been told I'm into book-writing myself?)

"Oh no need to look alarmed; I already have a publisher – Messrs Brunt & Badger. But now I can see you must be thinking me an old chatterbox and that it's time I got on with some teaching (as you forever were hinting at us in dear old Tampling St Nicholas days). But I can't help it; I love book-talk above all else. And there's none to be had in Sawpits.

"And you can send me a dozen of every book on your list and we'll chalk it up to the County Council at full retail price. No – make it a couple of dozen. *They* owe you plenty for what they put you through all that time ago. And I'll have Pintle send you his little book and we can meet on a Saturday and really go into things. Pintle likes to do the weekly shop in Barchester when the shelves are full so, while he's at it, the two of us can have some booktalk in that little bohemian teashop behind the Cathedral. Just the spot for a bit of literary chitchat."

Before leaving, I asked permission to test the children on *Horatius* and awarded the Blue Team two house-points. I was then escorted back into the playground and, as we skirted the coke-heap, she said, "I know I'm no Marilyn Monroe. And I suppose you can't imagine Pintle being in love. But he is. In fact, he has come to an arrangement with Mr Ireson at the memorial-yard and (though he dreads the day) if I pass away before him, Mr Ireson is to erect a marble one-shelf bookcase over me. Then, instead of flowers on his Sunday visit, Pintle will change a couple of my Brunt & Badger novels on the shelf so mourners can have a quiet read whilst hanging about for someone else's funeral to start. And he has put down a non-returnable deposit on this."

When Harpole told this astonishing news to Emma Foxberrow, he records that she irritatingly told him that, in the Great Womb of Time, the stars in their courses had marked the Pintles one for the other and was not he, Harpole, blind not to have spotted this? She then went on to extemporize indelicately on the honeymoon, neither of them (she claimed) knowing the facts of life "unless" she added, "one (A) of the Maharajah's 26 alphabetical wives had managed to drag young Pintle (B) behind his blackboard (C), whilst her husband (X) was busy laughing his head off pulling out bath-plugs."

Yet one man for one moment stood out from all the crowd,
Well known was he to all the three; they gave him greeting
loud.

PINTLE TO HARPOLE

I am informed by Mrs Pintle that interest has been evinced by
you in my little *Arithmetical Situations, a Moral, Mental and
Dramatic Approach by J. A. Pintle, FRIH.** I therefore venture
to submit its text to your judgement. Should you decide
against its literary or economic feasibility, I enclose a large
stamped and self-addressed envelope for its secure return.

As you will recall, I am one of The Old School and local
observation leads me to recognize that the current educational tide is set against such of us who linger on.
Nevertheless, like Mrs Thatcher, I conceive it no more than a
patriotic duty to stimulate and accelerate in Our Nation's
young, the mental energy, moral purpose, determination
and persistence under adversity which once made us the
envy and dread of other lands. Thus, if in its small way, my
monographic exercise advances her crusade of national
regeneration – sadly in abeyance – it will be enough.

As my dear parents so often reminded my greatly missed
sister, Diana, and myself (it was our family's favourite
hymn),

> Go labour on, spend and be spent,
> Thy joy to do the Master's will.
> Soon wilt thou hear the Bridegroom's Voice,
> The midnight peal, "Behold I come!"

---

* In antique times, when the very efficient teaching force had either only a
couple of years' institutionalized training or none at all, the better to
overawe credulous parents, practitioners added "letters to their name".
Pintle's letters mean either "Fellow of the Institute of Horticulture" or
"Institute of Hygiene".

And apropos this, Mrs Pintle's teaching career is not without its setbacks. In confidence, she is beset by a new breed of so-called educational advisers engaged by her employers to harass and humiliate her and her like by demanding attendance at in-service courses on so-called Modern Methods in making school-children happy. Happy! You will not be surprised that Mrs Pintle has not surrendered. Only last evening she said, "Well, George Harpole had his setbacks but, come what may, he stood his ground. And so shall I".

PS. I know that we had our little contretemps in the past, Harpole, but for me it is water under the bridge and, I trust, for you also.

Pintle's offering amounted to no more than a treatise scarcely of more than pamphlet length and in tripartite form in which,

(i) he explains his theory and
(ii) gives examples with detailed working and
(iii) 100 everyday problematical human situations requiring investigation and solution.

Initially, his proposal was that each problem (surprisingly, often having a mildly criminal tinge) must engage the interest of both student and explicator as a *moral* dilemma whose investigation and resolution demands protracted mental effort. Secondly, appealing to a reader's *mental* agility, he urges that there must be a physical enactment (ie, dramatization) of the situation for those pupils handicapped by a dulled imaginative perception. And, to this end, whatever was handy should be employed as stage props.

A single example will clarify this.

Supposing, for the purpose of Pintle's posed problem, the child is asked to discover how many trips a housemaid must make into a cellar so as to empty it of coal, the explicator must (a) *stimulate interest in the situation* by expounding the virtues of uncomplaining labour by the servant (A) and the domestic necessity urged by the mistress (B) of readying a household for a strike-ridden winter by stocking fuel whilst it was offered at summer prices and then (b) *dramatically* employing a pupil-nominee to impersonate the housemaid (A) urged on by a second impersonator of the mistress (B) to carry a wastepaper-basket (the coal-hod C), alternatively disappearing and re-appearing from behind the blackboard (the cellar, D).

Mr Pintle's text was succinct, its lay-out well ordered, its content deftly aimed at an identified body of likely purchasers. Without demur, the partners agreed its publication, directing Blow to fluff it out to a respectable bulk and weight by printing its text in large (18 point) Baskerville upon 2-sheet card. At Pintle's request, the book was dedicated to HRH the Maharajah, who graciously allowed his State Seal to be imprinted upon the book's dark-blue simulated snakeskin cover.

This unusual little primer never had more than respectable sales which gently diminished as the elderly head-teachers, who initially had ordered it, were forced into retirement or died. Reassuringly, an examination of H. & F.'s accounts confirms that not only were production costs covered but that the book made a modest contribution to the firm's survival.

And, oddly enough, like the American, Theodore Dreiser's Chicago Stockyard novel, *The Jungle* ("I aimed at their heads and hit their bellies"). Pintle enjoyed a similarly advantageous mis-hit. And by the literati! This merits comment.

It happened that, about this time, Professor Malc. Flecker published his much discussed (by other toilers in the fields of amaranth) *TLS* essay, *Whither Gurth the Swineherd?*, later collected into his symposium, *Distillations of Fictional*

Narrative. By and large, this piece was an unprovoked attack on the bumper novels of Sir Walter Scott. (Gurth, a Saxon serf, you will recall, is discovered idling in a landscape minutely described from page 1 to page 17.) Professor Flecker then extended his tirade to take in fictional works by Sir William Golding, Miss Charlotte Bronte and Mrs Henry Wood. His dubious argument was that these and several other properly highly regarded authors so glutted their readers with lavish dollops of descriptive narrative seasoned with so detailed analyses of their fictional characters' motives, that their admirers' imaginations atrophied from intellectual disuse. Thus, he pontificated, an astonishingly wide spectrum of readers visualised almost identically both the story's background and those persons inhabiting it. (At this point, he furnishes a statistical appendix prepared by students at the University of Ipswich.)

Contrasting this, the Professor cites the book-writers, Austen and Chaucer, claiming that their arid prose com-pelled their readers' supposition to range freely across the outward appearance (eye-colour, shoe-size etc.) of their fictional characters, their mental and moral processes, the motivation of their activities and the socio-economic and environmental background before which they moved, meditated and had their being. Finally, rendering down his argument to its essence, Flecker urges study of J. A. Pintle's seminal work (sic), his collected short stories, *Arithmetical Situations, a Moral, Mental and Dramatic Approach.*

He cites the book as "an interlinked series of circumscribed novellas so free of topographical background, physical and temperamental characterization that each reader (according to his/her imaginative resources) furnishes Pintle's barren tales with either the scantiest of stage-props or with rich fantasies of delight".

"How often eminent persons, Ministers of the Crown, skilful propellers of balls, ennobled crooks, media-battery force-feeders, confide airily that their reading is limited to accounts of extreme criminal or sexual activity. How often they explain that 'the book is un-demanding', 'after the real business of living, I need to bury myself in a book', 'a book helps me use up my time'. Small wonder that, in their turn and in their millions, their admiring countrymen similarly bury themselves in sumps of moral and mental degradation, barely able to stir their adiposed selves to prop ajar lolling chops for their daily TV and radio injections of regurgitated sit-coms and mindless howling. These are the nation's prize fatstock, once stuffed to bursting by Sir Walter, these are the disgusting litter spawned in his turn by Anthony Trollope and, in these degenerate days, by Wilbur K. Jakemannx, Junr Inc.

Britain's drug menace lurks not in Columbian poppy fields but in bookshop dumpbins, airport trash-spinners. Its pushers are profit-crazed publishers, corrupted writers and promotion-obsessed librarians. And, front-ing this tide of decay, stands but a wavering line of authors dedicated to a defence of what was, is and forever must be England's chiefest wealth – a fertile and vigorously creative literary imagination.

And, foremost at the breach, I number such as Miss Ivy Compton-Burnett who, in her numerous fictive works, eliminated all but conversation and, his back to hers, the disgracefully disregarded James Alfred Pintle.* And of this pair, Mr Pintle best exemplifies my argument: he has stripped his characters of *every* individual characteristic. But for this exciting innovator, even that is not enough:

* This flurry of publicity encouraged foundation of ABCX clubs in 23 identified locations (see Univ. of Ipswich Bulletin 2385). Their sole survivor meets on the first Thursday of each month in the Cobbett Hall, Burridge, Hants. Members take turns in providing and producing performances of their everyday domestic problems.

he has demanded the ultimate imaginative and exacting exertion from his readers. He has expunged even the *names* of his novellas' prime movers. We must make do with A, with B, with C and, in the author's darker passions, X.

Consider his story entitled *Problem No. 27*, admittedly one of his less exciting fictions,

At precisely 11.29 am, armed with a primed flintlock able to propel a ball at 300ft per sec, A begins a journey from Crewe Junction by LMSR to the Euston Main Line Terminus. This train maintains a constant speed of 63mph.

Thirty-four minutes later, apprised by electric telegraph of his enemy's departure and intent, B, secreting upon his person an elephant gun advertised by its manufacturers as having a missile propulsion-speed of 1,650ft per sec, departs from Euston towards Crewe in the cab of a privately hired locomotive travelling at 75mph.

As the two expresses pass, A fires ½ sec before B as each fatally discharges his weapon at the other.

(i) At what time did the two conveyances pass?
(ii) How far from Crewe Junction did the encounter take place? (Answer in mls, furs, chns, yds, ft.)
(iii) Which person perished first?
(iv) State arrival times of both bodies at their destinations.

This story exactly illustrates the Pintle Theory of Fictive Narration. You will observe that no explanation is given why A and B nurture murderous inclinations; there is no unhealthy gropings into their pasts to uncover the springs of their mutual enmity. Thus each reader may wander happily into a speculation of either A or of B's flawed persona. A fled mother? A dead mother? A dread mother? And, this resolved to his/her satisfaction, a reader then must decide upon one from limitless explanations of B's dislike of A. Boarding-school bully or victim? Dispossessed spouse? Discarded lover? Or was it no more than prolonged residence at Crewe Junction?

In one detail alone does Mr Pintle allow no leeway: his characters *always* are at odds one with the other. And this is what provides the almost unbearable tension to a Pintle plot. For let A build a defensive wall around his property but, on the instant, B digs a tunnel beneath it whilst, nocturnally, X dismantles the wall and fills in the tunnel. Let A endeavour to take a bath of fixed cubic capacity by turning on both taps but, immediately, B, employing one tap of superior velocity, fills his smaller bath. Meanwhile X takes it upon himself to remove both bathplugs . . .

Novelists, by the very title of their trade not unreasonably might be expected to make a gesture towards novelty. And this JAP patently has achieved: he modestly but triumphantly has advanced the frontiers of literature.

For, if his niche in literary annals should be disputed by drearily conventional authors and acidulated critics, nevertheless discover me a bookseller who does not venerate him as benefactor. Was it not J. A. Pintle who, at long last, delivered what Booksellers' Conferences annually have clamoured after? Was it not he who made it obligatory for the purchaser of *one* book to almost immediately purchase a *second?* And here I speak with utter certainty; whoever takes away *Arithmetical Problems, A Moral and Dramatic Approach,* within the hour will return for that other volume enigmatically entitled *Teacher's Copy with Answers.*

How influential was Professor Flecker's diatribe remains an imponderable. However, for some years, *The Pintle Syndrome* and its implications for modern writers merited a semi-module in the University of Ipswich's popular but unfortunately entitled workshop, *Every Eng Lit post-grad has some sort of a novel waiting to be evaluated.**

* The original printing error in the final word is corrected here.

PROCURATOR-GENERAL TO HARPOLE & FOXBERROW

Printed Works Copyright Act. Ed. VII 1908

At your expense and within 7 (seven) days despatch to our Privileged Seats of Learning at the Universities of Oxford, Cambridge, Edinburgh, Aberystwyth and to Trinity College, Dublin, Republic of Ireland, these literary works at no cost to me or to the universities named,

Pleasure Domes of Barset	*Jeffrey Amis*
Problem Arithmetic, a Moral, Mental and Dramatic Approach	*J. A. Pintle, FRIH*
The Bag Sinderby Church Choir's Fatal Noctambulation together with The Miraculous Salvation of Thos. Leaf	*Unattributed author*
The Book of British Satyrs	*Geo. Foxe*

G.H. to E.F.

He says he *has* to have them. Shall I send them?

E.F. to G.H.

No.

And for the holy maidens who feed the sacred flame
To save them from false Sextus, who wrought the deed of
*   shame.*

HARPOLE'S JOURNAL

As arranged, to Barchester and discovered the tea-room (Le Moulin) rendezvous tucked within a mews of sparky little boutiques, very cosy and snug with wicker chairs, check tablecloths, tastefully framed cathedrals and abbeys and nice motherly waitresses in aprons and caps. Had barely time to take it all in when Grace Pintle entered. Immediately began to weep bitterly.

"Oh, Mr Harpole" she sobbed, *"They* have had their way at last and I'm to be got rid of. *They* say my methods at Sawpits are bad for the children and that I am too set in my ways for retraining as a child-leader (which is their new name for teacher). They say I must choose either a Discretionary Lump Sum and reduced-pension or being taken on as a Child-pal (which is *their* name for attendance-officer).

"But you can't" I protested heatedly. "It is no sort of occupation for the gentler sex: they are forever being assaulted and not just by the parents of delinquent absentees but by the absentees. Why only last week in Barchester, when an attendance-officer approached a bunch who had seeped from their comprehensive into their truant-club, the new Shopping Mall, he was dumped into a shopping-pram and sent spinning to the hospital down the spiral car-exit. And *he* was a retired police-inspector."

"I love teaching" she wailed (but not over-loudly). I even liked it when Chadband gave me the Backwards for all those years. Teaching is my life. And Pintle will so miss going over my day as we sit at the hearth."

"It is hopeless" I counselled. *"They* are immovable. 'If the tree falleth to the south or unto the north, in that place where the tree falleth, there shall it lie.'* If that is what They have fixed-on, then that is *it*. So, come, let us look at the bright side. With your Lump Sum, you and Mr Pintle can buy a nice little villa with all modcons in an orange grove by the seaside of some Aegean island and live out your many remaining years in . . . well, in euphoria, I suppose. Think of the saving on heating bills, double-glazing etc – as well as not having to hang around airports, because you already will be on holiday."

Whilst advocating this, I poured her a cup of strong Darjeeling with three heaped spoonfuls of Demerara sugar which she absent-mindedly drank. This calmed her, thus providing a chance for her to dry her eyes and for me to eat a slice of caraway-seed cake.

"Oh" she said, "but I don't wish you to think that I am into teaching for the money. I am not one of the Grasping Society (though I shall still vote for Mrs Thatcher when she is back in the saddle again). We are not badly off. After all, as well as my own little sideline, there's Pintle's three pensions, the OAP, the teaching one and the little monthly nestegg his Maharajah still pops in the post. It's getting the sack that hurts. But, if anyone knows what that's like, it's you . . . all the children and their mums at Tampling St Nicholas looked up to you as a sort of godfather. But *They* still sacked you.

"Do not remind me, please" I said. "But to be charitable, if I'd hung on there, I should never have gone to Sinji – and the cricketing out there was splendid. Why, in the Dry Season, you could play not just a three but a 33 day match and not be rained-off. So let's look at what the future has in store for you. . . . This sideline you spoke of?

* For ref. see Alexander Cruden's Concordance to the Scriptures.

55

Grace Pintle giggled. "Well" she said, "because you ask me and only because you ask me, over the years I have been into this book-writing racket. But not under my own name. The chap who buys them from me and foists them off onto Boots calls them novels. But, really, they are just long stories. I do him two a year, one in summer for Christmas and one at Christmas for spring. It suits me very well . . . the seasonal rhythm, I mean."

This revelation astounded me. She paused, plainly not dissatisfied with the impression she was making.

"As a matter of fact, I happen to have a couple of the silly old things in my carrier-bag, if you would like to have a look at them. No, no, I don't expect you to read them here and now: you can take them away for a quiet browse. But now I know you will be agog to hear all the Tampling news."

She then told me that our late school-caretaker, Edwin Theaker, was a Socialist county-councillor and Chairman of the Education Committee and that the Abominable Croser was senior-lecturer in Modern Methods at a college-of-Education and how a chastened Councillor Mrs Blossom has been taken as his second wife by Mr Billitt, Billitt himself having been turned from his former ways by a wandering pair of Jehovah's Witnesses. ("Mind you" she tittered, "We all know whose bash it was that really turned him, don't we, Mr H.?")

And, in my turn, I related the political hullabaloo Miss Foxberrow had stirred up in Zanzambia. This set her laughing merrily. "You have been as good as a tonic" she told me as we arranged to meet in a fortnight's time, same hour same place and that, this time, Pintle should join us.

The reader must think that much of the preceding extract from Harpole's journal is irrelevant to a history of a publishing house. However, its inclusion has purpose: it confirms the trusting relationship, founded on times past, between Grace Tollemache and George Harpole. The succeeding several months which led to the writing and publication of *The Jessamy Brides* (for that, eventually, is where we shall arrive) were fraught with violent clashes of temperament between its author and Emma Foxberrow. And, such were the latter's quite outrageous demands upon Grace Pintle's integrity as a creative artist, that these would have brought about the novel's withdrawal but for its author's loyalty to her sometime headmaster, her trust in him as literary mentor and her admiration for him as man.

One supposes that it was on some quiet evening after a hard day on the road — let us say, at The Fleece in Thirsk's market-place or at The Swan in South Milford, that Harpole dutifully, even thankfully, laid aside the rep and assumed an editorial role. For, a couple of weeks' later, we find him writing,

> I got through *The Enslaved Heart* (by Jasmine Massingberd, one of Mrs P's noms-de-plume) in a single evening, finishing it off in bed. It is a moving episode in the otherwise sequestered life of a very respectable person in her middle years, Miss Ursula Everett-Morton. She is a certificated elementary-school teacher, not hand-some in a conventional sense but (we are told) with (unspecified) "tittilating characteristics".
>
> Whilst enjoying a well-earned and saved-up-for holiday, during the most fearful tempest since records began, she seeks shelter in an alp-top hut. The door is flung ajar and in reels a Tyrolese count "of ancient lineage". He is handsome in "a saturnine sort of way" and also very rich and Ursula immediately surrenders to his charms. When they exchange intimacies he is tender but demonstrates that he is no lounge-lizard by smashing a table with a single karate blow. (He is not

a vandal; the timber is needed as fuel for their fire.)

His military training saves the couple for, in his knapsack, he has a tin of pemmican and a bottle of champagne, also a multi-purpose knife which can open bottles. After a hearty meal and warmed up by the wine, he takes down a leopard skin hanging on the wall and, laying her gently upon it, exclaims, "Your lovely self kindles in me a flame like that of our little fire. But hotter. If what I am about to do appears unusual, it is nothing to what, in similar circumstances, more ignoble men would do when similarly inflamed. Whilst it is taking place, bear in mind that you are mine and shall be to the end of time."

But just when ("in the white heat of passion") their love is to be consummated, an elderly South Dakota (USA) missionary and his wife also seek refuge in the hut. Thus, they have to get up from the skin and sit around the fire and the four of them have an interesting discussion on the ordination of women-priests.

The count then partitions the hut with a rope from his knapsack and, the tiger-skin serving as a screen, they settle down for the night – the missionary's wife and Ursula on one side and the two men on the other.

Dawn breaks in radiant sunshine and, on the way down, the count describes his schloss and demands Ursula's hand in marriage. To this she warmly consents but, reaching the pension, they find a telegram saying that her widowed father, a retired railway-platelayer, has fallen downstairs. So, recognizing a daughter's duty, she hurries back to Swindon. Her several letters are un-answered. (She never learns that the count had fallen down a chasm.) So Ursula devotes her life first to the care of her father and also to the parochial church-council of which she is the hon sec.

It is some years since I last read a novel. In fact, the last was Josef Conrad's *Nostromo* (which was beyond me) and Kinglake's *Eothen* (which was not at all bad being about real life though some time ago), these being the two set-books we had to get through for school-certif. But now I realised that there was more to novels than meets the eye and eagerly began on Grace's second volume, *Slave of the Gods.*

Here, the heroine is Lucia Ravensthorpe-Pendragon, an infant-school headmistress who, at Brent Council's expense, visits Venice to do a feasibility-study of the Montesorri Method if employed in an inner-city situation. On the same course is a Spanish grandee, Don Pedro Qedinna-Silonia who, during a nature-walk, confides in Lucia that he is there only to learn how to supervise the education of his motherless child. (Although, actually, his wife is not dead but mad and confined to an attic. Lucia is not told this.)

During a free weekend, whilst botanising rock-scree plant habitats, Lucia drops into a ravine but clings to a shrub. Fortunately, Don Pedro who is hang-gliding, spots her and, swooping, soars to safety with Lucia in his arms. That evening, she comes down to dinner in an exotic après-ski outfit designed and run-up at evening-classes at her home-town (Bridlington) tech. He sees her in a new light – that is not only as one willing and able to teach his daughter elementary parsing, multiplication tables and so on but very well suited to solace his lonely nights. She at once agrees to this arrangement.

But, returning to the Venice Institute of Education, they find a new bunch of students has turned up and, amongst them, a man from Lucia's past from whom, still virginal, she fled on their wedding-night. (He had proposed trying out abominably unmentionable practises.) He now has a sociology PhD and is a Director of Education and threatens to expose her if she proceeds with her plan – ("Your bigamous escapade".) Leaving behind a grief-stricken note, she catches an early morning wagon-lit express and enters a C of E monastery in Rutlandshire.

This novel, I consider to be more mature than *Enslaved Heart*. Although it dwells on the pains and pleasures of love (with which I am not unfamiliar), no-one could possibly object to its presence on the shelves of a public library. However, so as to equip myself for giving its author a considered opinion of its literary worth, I took the precaution of looking up and memorizing other publishers' trade adverts for their books in *The Booktrader*.

When I reached our teashop on the succeeding Saturday morning, the Pintles already were there and I was welcomed with, "Pintle insists that the coffee and caraway-seed cake are on him. What did you think of them? I cannot wait to hear."

"Both novels are exquisite" I told her, "and the second is a work of rare genius. The reader inexorably is gripped as in a vice from Page One. It is a seminal work for all serious students of late 20th Century literature. Take that passage where Lucia tells her grandee, "I shall love and honour you and be tender and true. Then and only then, shall I have peace and heart's ease and no more pain. Heaven and I will watch over your motherless child. . . ." When I got to that paragraph, I had to put it (the book) down and compose myself: it is as good as a piece of poetry. Better, in fact, than this modern stuff."

"Why, Mr H." she exclaimed with great satisfaction, "You are word-perfect: there is no praise rings truer for us authors than to hear our own voice speaking."

"And what is your opinion, J.A.P.?" I asked.

"Oh Pintle likes them well enough" she replied. "But they're a bit on the fast side for you, aren't they Pintle? Too blue for you, eh? Yes, he says, they are. In fact, when I got Ursula down on the leopard skin up on that alp, it was Pintle who insisted on me bringing on those spoilsport Yankees. But your real grouse is the books not having my real name on them, isn't it? You'd like the covers to say they're written by Grace Tollemache wouldn't you? Or is it Grace Pintle?"

Pintle blew into his moustache – a sure sign, I recalled, of extreme annoyance.

"But I tell him (Don't I Pintle?) that my publishers, Brunt & Badger's contract says that their editor must choose an author's name to fit a book's title. Pintle did write to them. (Quite a stiff letter wasn't it Pintle?) and they answered that, if someday, someone writes up my life, they, Brunt & Badger, would have no objection (in principle) to it being hinted that, on the quiet, I write all my novels. We've brought you three or four more, by the way."

And, taking his cue, Pintle passed over a Tesco carrier-bag filled with books.

"There are 27 in all" she went on. "But I am not all that struck with the first nine or 10. They don't cut near enough the bone, although Pintle swears they're the best things I've done."

We then settled down to our coffee and the seed-cake. This particular cake was not up to my mother's mark. But to be fair, it wasn't too bad.

This account of Grace Tollemache-Pintle's involvement with H. & F. will be of unusual interest to literature departments since, oddly enough, few records exist of preliminary encounters (on an equal basis that is) between publisher and author. And it is for this reason that I shall elaborate what to a casual reader, may seem insignificant happenings. For instance . . .

Later pages of his journal confirm that, on sales trips, Harpole did read the five or six novels but with decreasing zest. On June 11th, we find him querulously writing,

Finished *Forsaken, Forsaken* at 11.32 am whilst snatching at a sandwich in Hope Bowdler, Salop, churchyard, en-route to the Castle Bookshop, Ludlow. Must her heroine *always* have to be a middle-aged school-mistress? Broke my thermos tripping over the porch boot-scraper.

And on June 23rd at The Red Lion, Sherburn-in-Elmet, making for Godfreys at York. . . . Found *Elfin Horn* vaguely unsatisfactory. Whenever there is likelihood of a mild bit of love-making, you can bet your boots on a visitor bargeing in . . . even here in the middle of the Gobi Desert, earlier described as having "lone and level sands stretching faraway. . . ."

and, on July 4th, at The Falcon, Fotheringhay (visiting the Oundle Bookshop) . . .

Sometimes I wish her heroes could be normal chaps like me. They forever have an hyphenated surname or some title a step up from Mr and have film-star faces. And not a one of them seems to have a 8-5.30, Monday to Friday job.

Nevertheless, when loyally reporting to Emma Foxberrow, he didn't dwell upon such reservations and was put out when she claimed that Grace T.-P.'s secret literary persona did not astonish her in the least.

HARPOLE'S JOURNAL

Emma told me anyone with half an eye in his head must see "the poor old thing dwells in Dreamland" and insisted that her trouble was not shunting her Dad the Alderman into Sheltered Accommodation early enough and then dragging Pintle into the spare bedroom whilst there still was some frisk and fire in his poor old bones. Then (she claimed) there wouldn't be any need to work out her frustrations by churning out drivel. ("*The Enslaved Heart! Forsaken,*

Forsaken! Ha!*) When next you have one of your cosy little lit-sit-ins, tell her to fall off Cloud Nine and rub her nose in Life-as-it-really-is."

And Harpole, fair-minded as ever, must have brooded on these strictures and allowed merit in them. More of this later.

---

* Both novels later were made into tremendously successful films. *Enslaved Heart* won Oscars for Best Script and Best Moral Content.

Far o'er the crashing forest, the giant arms are spread
And the pale augurs, muttering low, gaze on the blasted
*   head.*

To ready myself for this unfamiliar employment, the pre-
paration of a commercial-history, I have studied several
publications — admittedly more lavishly produced (being
enviably subsidized by privatized monopolies and, thus able
to commission practised and prestigious authors) yet,
basically, with a similar aim — to tell a matter-of-fact tale. But I
was struck by a constant feature — the business's prime-
mover, whether founder, chairman or managing-director,
seemed to have only a "business-life". None gardened,
played golf, went to church, wrote furious letters to the
council, endured traffic-jams, had difficult children or
contentious husbands/wives. I received an impression that
their lives unnaturally were totally devoted to business.

This manifestly is ridiculous. For instance, in several
instances, the unrevealed ends of these industrial moguls, by
shot-gun, rope or razor, was brought about by utterly
uncommercial reasons . . . one, I recall, could not endure life
after the death of a much-loved cat.

And this has served me as salutary warning to portray at
least one of the H. & F. partners in a human perspective and
thus not wholly pre-occupied with the book-trade. So, now
and then, I mean to let the real, the essential everyday George
Harpole speak for himself of the trivial events which occupy
all of us when we are living and "making a living". Here
(perhaps an extreme example) is that other Harpole, Blow's
unwilling successor as Jordans Bank churchwarden,

   "Wrestling with income-tax return. Hammering at front

door. Found Mrs Bickerdyke, lately removed from Blackburn, Lancs, who does a weekly dust-and-sweep of our ancient place of worship. "Oh, Mr Harpole" she cried, "Oh, come quick; there are awful goings-on in your church."

Immediately ran, following her down the road. Pushed open the door. Long-haired chap in Maoist tunic, presumably one of the new activist teachers we read about, intoning his approval of our Roubilliac monument (1752) to Sir Justinian Bosanquet. Those of his pupils not staring drearily at ceiling were doing nothing more anti-social than trying on our lady-choristers' cassocks. In fact, the only occurrence in a sacred edifice I could take exception-to (these days, that is) was a young ruffian who had jammed a respectable-looking girl into our pulpit and, with a hand over her mouth, was fumbling at her shirt.

"I cannot interfere" I whispered to Mrs Bickerdyke. "As an ex-acting-headmaster, it would be against professional protocol, because I am convinced the teacher cannot help but see what is going on and has decided on a policy of non-involvement. And, of course, it may be that the couple in the pulpit are rehearsing a scene from their annual school-play . . . perhaps a scene between Desdemona and Othello."

"No, not them," she hissed. "THEM!"

To my astonishment, I now noticed two grossly overfed oafs, prize specimens of commercial TV's pigs-at-the-trough, prising open our alms-for-the-poor-box with the castbrass crozier-topped vicar's warden's staff. What then ensued was even more amazing. Mrs B. rushed forward to land an almighty flat-hander across one youth's face and, at the same time, cleverly wresting the staff-of-office from his mate's grasp.

"Take that — you horrible defiler of this hallowed place" she cries and, with the sharp end of the pole, makes a shrewd thrust at his belly. Domino! Not only does she skittle her second victim (who satisfactorily clatters his skull on a corner of our font's pedestal) but the ruffian in our pulpit relaxes his grip and immediately is bitten by the dauntless girl, causing him to scream in pain. Culture-seekers forsake their teacher and rush to view their stricken mates.

However, to my professional disgust and disbelief, even without an audience, the teacher continues monotonously to extol the merits of Roubilliac, informing the air that "he is part of our English Heritage. But for creative geniuses such as he, we should not be the nation we are. . . ."

"It's OK now, Mr Harpole" Mrs Bickerdyke said. "We both can go home. And if they have me up in court, I shall plead that it was God manifesting Himself here below in the unworthy form of His servant Lucy, down fra' Lancasheer."

"Well done! Oh, well done!" I enthused. "At a single blow, you have converted me to the cause for the ordination of women-priests. But − one small detail − from your words, am I to believe that you suppose God to be masculine?"

"Oh yes, most certainly, Mr Harpole" she answered earnestly, "Up i' Lancasheer, we wouldn't have Him anything else. Up theer, it's a man's world."

On the housetops was no woman but spat toward him and
    hissed,
No child but screamed out curses and shook its little fist.

Expenses were high, income low and spasmodic. Anxiously concerned enquiries were made by the elderly administrator of the Foxberrow Grandchildren's Trust and Emma, shaken from her usual disregard of money (whence it came and where it went), to save postal charges, sent review copies of Shutlanger's *Story for the English* to only those half-dozen journals subscribed by a closed circuit of Church of England professionals — *The Steadfast Worshipper's Monthly, The Altar-Server's Quarterly* and *The Church's one Foundation,* an annual, and the like. She could not be expected to know that, by and large, these periodicals had no counter sales, miserably threadbare subscription lists and circulated chiefly in common rooms of theological colleges.

In their turn, editors forwarded the book to retired clergy-men who, for no more reward than wifely admiration and a proper gratification at seeing their names in print as con-firmation that they still were alive, happily furnished a couple of hundred carefully considered words. Of these scattered seeds, two sank into sloughs of silence, three, although unread, were listed, according to the season, under such conscience-salving headings as RECOMMENDED READING for CHRISTMAS/EASTER/WHITSUNTIDE and these, by giving the publishers' address, at least served as a free small advert.

But three fell upon fruitful ground.

"Gleaner" in *Church Union Commentary* seems to have become so incensed by H. & F.'s offering that, by para three, he and his argument parted company,

"We would have supposed that at least one of this new publishing house's directors, E. P. Foxberrow, an Oxford double-first and a member of my own college, might have recognized Mr Shutlanger's book to be an affront not only to ministers of religion but even to those of his countrymen who regrettably cross a church's thresholds but twice – initially to breathlessly yell their heads off as baptismal water is wasted upon them and, finally out of breath, are trundled in on some undertaker's trolley.

It might be argued that this faithless crew cannot be expected to succour a Mother Church they have forsaken and a Bible from which they seek comfort only as a draught-excluder when the central-heating breaks down. But then, neither did their 16th Century forefathers, scrambling like baboons, up trees and pinnacles, the better to gawp at the glorious agonies of our English martyrs.* One supposes that these bird-brained voyeurs had swallowed Authority's word that, if a man grows spiritually fat, the holiness must be roasted out of him."

And he fired a departing shot.

"Mr Shutlanger is described as a Grammar School headmaster. But, if one may judge from the anacolutha and anaphora littering his prose writings, whatever else may be taught in his establishment, grammar no longer is."

There is merit in what one charitably supposes may have been swilling around "Gleaner's" muddled head – for instance, his contention that Emma Foxberrow, a naturally contentious person with scant regard for the susceptibility of

---

* Gleaner may have had in mind William Sawtrey, a Norfolk Lollard parson, who, in 1401, after trial by the Archbishop of Canterbury, was burnt in chains. He had persisted in declaring that communion bread in the mouth was still bread, that money lavished on self-protective pilgrimages was better spent on the poor and that men were more worthy of adoration than angels. Shutlanger, however, rebutted this, declaring that it was an ancestor of Gleaner, an early member of the High Church Union, who had struck the first medieval match to ignite Sawtrey.

others, having pushed a book upon the well-mapped mine-field of holy ground, should not have foreseen peril ahead. But what is more astonishing is that she did not recognize Gleaner's rumble as forewarning a coming storm. Even brief apprenticeship in the book-trade cannot excuse her of such heedlessness.

And this shifty letter is unconvincing,

EMMA FOXBERROW TO FELICITY FOXBERROW,
. . . far-off Tampling days, my opinion of Harpole's pal, Shutlanger, was that he was a boor and a boreing boor with a pass-degree brain at that. And here, on Jordans Bank, when we ran into him again, time and tribulation had taught him nothing. OK . . . OK . . . Then why, knowing this, did I agree to take aboard his book?

Good question, my girl.

Because and only because we had to have a book and, like the cat, that book lay on our mat. Yes, yes, I was told that its content was "of a religious nature". But God only knows religion's harmless enough. So OK, I didn't read it. And, to tell truth, my sole reservation was its brevity. In trade jargon, it was "a slim volume" when if Shutlanger *had* to rewrite the Bible, what we needed was a fat, latter-day *The Explicit Confessions of Potiphar's Wife, Nymphomaniac-Extraordinaire* (Sale to juveniles forbidden). But I do recall the thought, Well it won't cost much in typesetting and paper and we're bound to learn something from the publishing process . . . Felix don't! I'll say it for you – WELL WE CERTAINLY LEARNT.

I must confess sympathy for E.F. For, had events run a normal course, a first book – and a theological one at that – might have been expected to be barely noticed. And, for some weeks it was – loitering unwept, unhonoured and unsung in the doldrums, as this sales' report shows,

Sales to public libraries	7 copies
To theological institutions	4 copies
To church bookstalls	2 copies
To bookshops	15 copies
	(all to Mrs Fazackerly)

Then, one month later, a second and final notice of the book's publication appeared in *The Gospel Seminaries Earnest Inquirer, Vol. xxiv.* And, for a scholarly quarterly, Professor H. J. Slazenger's essay is unusually readable.

Let us consider a single incident illustrative of the book's flavour. Thisman and his sorry band have reached London and attend a musical concert in the Albert Hall (pp 42/3). I quote,

Chap. 6. v. 35. And they spake saying It is the Feast of the Last Night of the Proms and these, the young men and maidens of our people, cry aloud for chariots of fire, burning spears and other light arms. Is not this that great outpouring of the spirit of which you prophesied?

v. 36. And he answered them saying Where are those skinny kids with empty bloated black bellies I beheld in the wilderness and stony places of Breakfast TV before that commercial of rolypoly whiteskins with snouts in their trough grunting More Mum give us more?

v. 37. And they answered him not a word but straightway they departed and came unto Putney.

Yet despite numerous similar incidents in this unusual book, I must emphasise most emphatically Thisman never identifies himself with Our Lord. His fanatical half-educated supporters may do so. But Thisman never!

Nevertheless, we are left with the nagging impression that his rabble of recruits *did* suppose that they were witnessing a Second Coming.

Mr Shutlanger has put before us a challenging story. His is a bold – perhaps overbold – bid to bring the Gospel's uncompromising message not only to our countrymen who pay little more than lip-service to our Christian Faith but also to those parsons who neither fill buildings with bodies nor hearts with spiritual sustenance.

I warmly recommend this book to any reader who, in Christian charity, finds himself able to discuss its mortal message with his immortal soul.

The following week five more copies were sold to university divinity departments bringing total sales to 33.

These two notices were all that could be hoped for and, to disperse the common belief by authors that no effort had been made to promote their books,* George Harpole delivered photo-copies of them to Shutlanger and commiserated with the author at the neglect of *The Story* by both national Sundays and dailies, adding that, until now, he always had looked upon The Press with respect.

To which Shutlanger is reported to have replied, "Really! You constantly astonish me, Harpole. The Press! *You* may call it The Press; *I* call it Paston. And every and each school has its Paston. Paston idles, Paston fidgets, Paston is shiftless and, if Paston thinks, it is only to think what idiotic triviality *he* could utter next. Paston does not pass his school-certif."

And, lapsing into the lingo of his own *Story,* he added, "And the Press beheld Paston and knew him and claimed him for her own. Harpole, Paston is the Press; the Press is Paston."

Sensibly, Harpole took this outrageous pronunciamento with a pinch of salt and, whenever opportunity presented itself, diligently pressed Shutlanger's interests upon whoever crossed his sales path. To whit . . .

---

* From times immemorial, authors have distrusted their publishers. In the 1992 Spring number of The Society of Authors' journal, a practised writer informs aspirants that publishers employ illiterates because "it makes them feel better about their own disabilities" and that some publishers are either dyslexic or find reading so difficult that they turn down books without looking at them. Finally, he urges authors to treat some publishers as mentally ill and thus meriting kindness and understanding.

On trade-route to Far West, took pub lunch at Stow-on-the-Wold with prestigious Oxford University Press rep. Was told that X, the top critic of the top Sunday lived nearby in his Cotswold mansion and it would be worth my while trying my luck for as little outlay as a bottle of Californian Cabernet Sauvignon packaged with a review copy of Shutlanger's book.

Discovered X not in mansion but in Olde Post Office. Also in violent row with wife. "Look here, you layabout," X's wife was raving, "Withers definitely won't chalk a ha'poth more on the slate so, if you want your supper, he'll need at least a fiver. What about flogging this *Kingsley Amis* and that *Antonia Fraser* and we could chuck in a couple of *Fred Bugginses* for good measure. Fosco'll fork out a fiver for that lot: he can't help but get full retail price for one of 'em in his bookshop."

Don't be so b***** stupid" X yells back. "There'd be hell to pay if Old Rhino's not reviewed.* Look here, you can flog these three first novels and we'll chuck in half-a-dozen b***** old Brunt & Badgers'.

When Mrs X had gone off, he waved at sofafull of review copies. "How do they expect me to get through 'em" he complained. "I'm not a f****** reading-machine. There aren't enough hours in a day even if I gave up eating and sleeping."†

Asked him if the books' unreviewed authors didn't lie on his conscience.

"Nobody asked them to write the d***** things" he sneered. Then relented. "Well, now and then, I knock off a line or

---

* Customarily, literary editors dare not withhold from sole review bad novels by highly regarded authors. For a new or little known novelist's book to appear on such a week is a disaster: there will be no space left.

† By Ancient Custom & Practice, book-reviewers are paid a uniform fee whatever the length of a book. Thus very long books are rarely read but given compensatory vague and inoffensive notices.

two. (It's amazing what you can squeeze out of a blurb.) And then there's always other chaps' reviews to fall back on. Anyway, nowadays, you can just about tell what's inside it from a book's title. Never had but the one complaint. Misread a field-marshal's autobiog as *Haste to the Bottle.* But it's usually enough to thumb-flick the pages for most of the aura to seep and leak out. Then you just encapsulate it. Mind you it needs years of practice. . . ."

Glimpsed my wares. "Ah!" he cried, "B***** old *Foxe's Martyrs,* eh? Can't beat buckets of blood to keep a book in print! Ah, here's the wife back from the takeaway. . . ."

Discreetly stripped Shutlanger's book of all but its jacket and wrapped it round the bottle. Left it on his sofa.

Then, at last, without hope of further sales, Emma Foxberrow remaindered the edition, offering *Shutlanger* to the trade at 20 pence apiece but, except for an order from Mrs Fazackerly for ten volumes, the offer was not taken up. So the partners agreed (1) Blow should dump all unbound copies on the Council tip, (2) 50 bound copies should be donated to the Church Organ Fund for raffling and (3) a final 29 books put aside against tardy orders from British Council outposts.

And thus, sadly, Shutlanger's *Story* stole into that vast silence where, in a pulped limbo, many a writer's chastened hope (save in a spouse's heart) withers, droops and dies.

But . . .

But Ed Helidon's Top of the Ratings TV Show's stream of theatrical and political supplicants pleading for self-exposure dried up.

This phenomenon has been variously explained by (a) the more aggressive PR agents taking prolonged Caribbean vacs at the same time, by (b) a scarifying attack on a royal drone by a Militant Tendency activist treacherously infiltrated into the

Show by a Marxist cameraman, by (c) an airline strike which marooned bodies kept in a deep-freeze for such crises by New York's Rentashowbizz, Inc. ("Those on our books with tiny tiny brains have big big bosoms.")

Be that as it may, the Show's frenzied researchers, drawing blank in normally well-stocked coverts, *The Times* Diary, the *Telegraph's* Peterborough, *The Spectator* Diary etc, in mounting panic probed into deep provincial undergrowth. And came upon *The Barset Weekly Messenger's* "Highways & Hedges", a column cobbled together by a freelance, Ginchy Montagu (née Trigger). This young person to raise to subsistence-level the stipend of her husband, a parson, earned lineage by reporting WI Knitting marathons, roll-calls of mourners, petty-sessions misdemeanours and such. And she, whilst tidying the study, had lighted upon Professor Slazenger's review of *The Story*.

She knew that Mr Bloom's business had been taken over by someone from Away and immediately dashed over to Tampling where an unusually co-operative Shutlanger. . . . But let her piece speak for itself.

HEADMASTER SAYS BRITS BRAINLESS
Edwin Shutlanger, celebrated local scribe, denied that he was cast down by his book's poor sales, asserting that, despite 118 years of free public education, two-thirds of Brits can only sound out single syllable words like b-u-m and b-l-o-o-d.

"I definitely know of one so-called newspaper with a circulation of millions" he told me, "where each Monday morn that ever dawns, its Proprietor pens his staff, from editor to office-boy, into a Thought Room. Then, when a hooter goes off and, in time with a macho-machine, they all do thirty push-ups shouting PUSH THEIR SNOUTS INTO BREASTS . . . BUMS . . . BUTTOCKS . . . BLOOD.

Then they all scuttle off and do just that (dishing out a double dose on the Sabbath)."

Mr Shutlanger continued, "God alone knows *The Story* was spelled out for simpletons. But I forgot that illiteracy is spreading faster than the Balance of Payments gap. So my wife, who does a bit of sketching, plans to re-draw my books as *The Story for the English in Pictures.*

He reeled and on Herminius he leaned one breathing space.
Then, like a wild-cat mad with wounds, sprang right at
Astur's face.

The Ed Helidon researcher who came across Ginchy
Montagu's piece was a bright Bible-bred girl, beady-eyed
enough to spot manna whilst it still loitered at cloud level:
she alerted an assistant producer. The time could not have
been more propitious. A racehorse trainer scheduled to
appear on The Show having been advised by his solicitor
that, pending police enquiry, he was likely to appear
elsewhere, had scratched. And, on the instant, Shutlanger
was offered a couple of thousand pounds, full legal
indemnity and door-to-door transport.

It is no more than fair to explain that, although Helidon
had never heard of Shutlanger, neither had Shutlanger heard
of Helidon. And had not Harpole reminded him of Publishers' Standard Contract Clause 6a ("The author agrees to
undertake reasonable engagements to publicize his Work or
Works"), he would have refused to go.

But go he did.

Now The Helidon Show had perfected a bulls-eye/dead-
cert degradation-routine which went like this,

− Subject isolated in hospitality-chamber,
− Subject 75% anaethetized with booze and bonhomie,
− Subject aimed and propelled down ramp,
− Subject 100% destabilized by quadraphonic applause,
− Subject collapsed into luxury leather low-slung sofa,
− Subject shredded into object by Show's depersonalizing
  processor.

Then for
− 50 secs, Object reminded who she/it/he was.

— 300 secs, Object (1) flattered (2) beguiled (3) cajoled (4) hectored, (5) brow-beaten into indiscreet, belittling idiocies.

— 25 secs, Object congratulated upon his acuity, object rewarded with signed portrait of Mr Helidon. Object pitched back into obscurity.

Never having witnessed such a performance and wonder-struck why (even as a headmaster) his appearance should percussion thunderous acclamation, flashing lights and organ peals, Shutlanger, stewed in free licquor and out of control, reeled downhill towards his research-attested audience of 13½ millions. Until, blinded, deafened and missing a step, he bullocked into the sofa's back, cannoned headfirst over it and, flattening Helidon, sledged across the floor into a buffer of front-row legs and genuine real-life cheering.

On his knees, but like a drowning mariner, clinging to his mike, Helidon breathlessly began an already out-of-date welcome until Shutlanger, on his back and seeing his tormenter through a sodden haze, violently yelled, "What is Britain's Best-selling Book?"

Ed, recognizing an outsize problem on his hands, squeezed out a grapefruit grin and quipped lightly, "Oh, any old thing by Billy Shakespeare, Jeff Archer, Cathy Cookson . . . oh and . . . Robinson Crusoe." (Merry applause.)

But Shutlanger, levered to his feet by an encouraging couple of OAPs (up for the day by BR Cheap Day Return from Basingstoke) and wiping his ragged moustache with the back of a hairy hand, had shuffled forward and, at close quarters and in dead silence, was examining his host with intense interest. Then, shaking his head, he murmured, "Ed, you are off your orange." And, turning to his audience (now grown to 16,000,000), in tones of deep solemnity, he pronounced, "The best-selling book is The Bible."

(Respectful applause.)

And I have re-written it."

(Prolonged applause.)

"But are there not already several up-to-date versions?" asked Helidon, sidling back into his Show. "And by *experts?*" (a shrewd thrust).

"Sixteenth Century folk talked like their Sixteenth Century Bible," Shutlanger trumpeted. "And this is OK . . . that is OK. But nowadays, who but academic zombies talk like their academic concocted abominations? Whereas my *Story* is in supermarket-talk, football terrace (without the bad language) talk and neighbours-over-the-fence talk."

Then, allowing time for this pronouncement to sink into the nation's head, he added triumphantly, "Mind you, you'll find all the 'Thees' and 'Thous' 'verily, verilys' and 'per-adventures' still there . . . for the sake of the old folk."

(*Voice from back*) − "Don't forget the 'And it came to pass's', sir. And the 'Woes unto ye' and all those 'hundred-folds', sir."

(Ovation.)

"And also" Shutlanger went on, nodding approval at his unseen supporter, "And also for the sake of the saintly old parson up the road who always was good for a couple of quid when the nipper's boot-soles wore out in a bad winter."

(Standing ovation.)

Then, rudely shoving Ed aside, he closed in on the camera and menaced the nation. "Yes, you lot in the Outer Darkness, those of you who aren't goggling at little balls being knocked up green baize and down fairway greens. . . . Yes, you! You're not here forever. How will it be with you when there's that tap on your shoulder and a Voice murmurs, 'This night thy soul (or what's left of it) shall be required of thee.' Then what? What then?"

(Unearthly silence.)

(Uneasy applause.)

"This godless but not God-forsaken land needs my *Story*. You snob town-planners in rural ex-rectories who've shoved other folk's poor old mums up 17 floors! And you disgusting yobs who frighten the living daylights out of them when they're trapped there! You motorway slaughtermen! You asset-strippers of poor men's jobs! You swine (who the Gadarene herd would have backed off from) who batter the fruit of your loins or demand the NHS do a free job murdering someone else's! You supermarket defilers of the Sabbath! You politicians with sticky fingers in half-a-dozen honey pots, who'd sell your grandmas for a mess of potage at Buck House! You banks and building societies that lend and lend and cast and cast your debtors out of their semis and into the street! You dead-faced directors of collapsing companies voting yourselves long pay-packets against the day when you'll need to buy short sentences!

"I wrote *The Story* for you.

"Now let him that can read, read it."

(Tumultuous cheers, foot-stamping, whistling, two or three Alleluias.)

And Shutlanger reeled forward once more and, Helidon's guests making way for him like old-time royalty, slumped into a front seat. And slept.

(Next day, the young beady-eyes, Bible-bred researcher was sacked.)

But meanwhile axe and lever right manfully have been plied
And now the bridge hangs tottering above the boiling tide.

Subsequent events are well documented. TV, radio, the Press, scrambled for copies of *The Story* and, finding none in bookshops, pursued it to Jordans Bank. There, Mrs Shutlanger remaindered her 50 copies at £100 apiece and, recovering those set aside for an Organ Fund raffle, raised the going-rate to £150. And sundays and dailies alike, refusing its review to mild-mannered literary editors, turned it over for carving to butchers from Features. And these tossed out raw gobbets like,

> Chap. 3 v. 17. And behold they tarried by a wayside church. And he said What is that painted window? And they answered him saying It is a beautiful stained-glass Flying-Fortress. For many went forth from this place to burn and blast the enemies of Our Lord and King. Yea also their women and children leaving not one stone standing upon another in all their land. And this window is to the Glory of God.
>
> v. 18. Then Thisman cried out with an exceeding loud voice saying My House is become a butcher's billboard. And he cast a stone and lo the window was rent in twain. Then they straightway departed and came unto Milton Keynes.

and

> Chap. 6 v. 6. And as they journeyed from Golders Green unto Hampstead behold a great multitude was gathered about the dwelling of a Minister of the King yea some upon the roof thereof. And they that were about the gate answered him saying This man hath done evil in

the sight of the *Sun* for he hath served an idol in a massage-parlour. And these are the servants of the *Mirror,* the *News of the Worlds* yea even the *Daily Telegraph* come to cast down his image.

v. 7. Then Thisman spake saying Let him that is without sin fiddling his bimbo onto his expense-claim take the first snap. And straightway and with one accord they all departed each man into his innermost darkroom.

So Shutlanger's *Story for the English* went off like the discharge of a duck-gun: its spread of shot was awesome. Not just a buzz there and sting here: the hive was blasted and its maddened swarm scattered. IT WAS SENSATIONAL.

The Established Church was not amused to discover its Primate cast in the role of Lord Chief Justice Priest and its General Synod baying for blood. The identification of the C-in-C American Advanced Strike Force as a spittle-image of Pontius Pilate washing his hands of Thisman's elimination brought a sharp note from the White House reminding the Prime Minister that Britain's five-year license as "Most Favored Nation" would soon be coming for reassessment.

And perhaps it was spite that provoked two editors (who continually had been ignored for ennoblement) to headline Thisman's outrageous version of The Magnificat — "He hath cast down the Mighty from their Palace and hath exalted the humble and meek into its conversion into flats."

I quote at random . . .

Proprietors of chain-groceries generating immense family fortunes — ("Man shall not live by sliced-bread alone . . ."), property billionaires — ("The bribes paid to corrupted councillors shall be the cornerstone of their prosecution" . . .), ennobled chairmen of public enterprises they helped privatize — ("No man can serve two masters: ye cannot serve the taxpayer and Mammon except in jail.")

It is said that the Union of High Church Priests and the

81

Federation of Chief Constables told the Home Secretary he must resign or prosecute over,

> Chap. 23 v. 32. A certain rep went down from Blackburn unto Brum and fell among thieves who stripped him of his raiment, his credit-cards his samples and his Volvo and left him half-dead. And by chance a certain high-church vicar came that way to cast out women from the General Synod and when he saw him he accelerated into the fast-lane. Likewise a Chief Constable came and looked severely upon him and booked him for loitering upon a public highway.
>
> But a scrapload of hippies as they journeyed to the Stonehenge Summer Solstice Feast of the Cracked Skulls came where he was and when they saw him they had compassion on him and bound up his wounds and had a whip-round for Lord Forte to put him up in his travel-lodge.

The *Story's* discharge hit friend and foe alike with splendid abandon, jerking readers from secret joy at another's discomfiture to outrage on recognizing themselves several verses on. Feminists, for instance, jubilant at Shutlanger's version of The Jar of Spikenhard were infuriated by his interpretation of the Parable of the Ten Virgins.

Retaliation was not slow: Authority concentrated a massive PR cannonade against the lone target. The Minister of Education promised ("under the meaning of the Act") to look into Shutlanger's fitness to conduct a school's daily "Act of Worship". Young university dons were promised interminable tenure and prime TV time to demonstrate the imbecility of Shutlanger's parallels and the Lord Chancellor hinted a guarded opinion of a likely breach of the ancient law of blasphemy in,

> v. 9. And Thisman asked those that were round about him What is that hanging round the Lord-bishop's neck

as he comes forth from his palace. And they answered him saying It is the cross upon which One died.

v. 10. Then Thisman lifted up his voice and cried bitterly It was not like that. It was not like that at all. It was a bad and bloody business.

Nor was the fizzing bomb defused by a TV sermon preached by the Archbishop of Canterbury, declaring that, although there was grave danger of *The Story* being read by the wrong readers and, for that reason, better banned, he personally had forgiven Shutlanger and called upon viewers to pray for him and all other unsuitable members of The Society of Authors.

This mild rebuke fell upon deaf ears and Rentamob took over. By popular demand subsequent eruptions have been shown repeatedly on all TV channels during dull intervals between political back-stabbing, sexual aberration in high places, multiple murders and mean little wars, so that no more than the barest summary need concern us here. For instance,

An export load of skinheads, dressed down to their doc-martens in union-jacks, was rejected as sub-standard at Cherbourg and shipped back to Southampton. There, their driver, fearing for his coach, off-loaded them at Dorchester, lying that Shutlanger was a native of that pleasant place. But a brave business-man (Mr R. S. V. Somerville) infiltrating the horde, cleverly offered Thomas Hardy as scapegoat – he not only being a book-writer and godless but handy. This daring fellow lured them from their proposed pillage of the town's new hyper-market and across two planning-blights to TH's monument (erected by public subscription) where they tore off that worthy's head and, honour assuaged, bore it to Liverpool spiked on an uprooted Belisha Beacon.

Naturally, there was the regulation quota of copycat book-burnings, an interesting example taking place in front of the Strict Covenanter Tabernacle at Gilliecranky Junction.

There, its minister, having first alerted the *Stirling Advertiser,* learned too late that *The Story* could not be bought in Scotland. But, under plain cover, his wife cleverly substituted *John Knox's Sermons against Women* from the vestry library. This was smouldered. ("A didna ken hoo non-combustible was a buik.") There were bonfires in towns without bookshops (or even a W. H. Smith), the most bizarre incineration being at Great Minden, where an out-of-date *Brindle's Landed Gentry* was donated by the Squire.

In Birmingham, police forced back immense crowds demanding Shutlanger's or, if unavailable, Mr W. H. Smith's blood and these only dispersed when a dauntless WHS spokeswoman explained that her company's policy had been, was and forever would be a refusal to entertain books from small publishers not on their Authorized Purchasing List and, in any case, Mr Smith had removed to a better place. The mob then moved upon Waterstone's but were frustrated by a resourceful manager (fiction) who, like Zaccheus, climbed into a tree to shout that *The Story* had disappeared even from the fiche.

Day upon day, the uproar, briskly fanned by Press and TV, flourished until one might have supposed that the Jordans Bank publishers, confused and awed by immense offers from conglomerates for re-publication serial rights, digested editions and firm offers to buy the firm to get the book, very sensibly might have fled into hiding.

Instead, Harpole & Foxberrow admirably demonstrated the only effective policy against persistently unreasonable demands – Silence! But when, later, this was remarked upon, Emma Foxberrow disarmingly confessed, "Sadly – no. We had no such policy: we were *stunned* into silence."

MINUTES OF MEETING

Present — Miss E. F. Foxberrow, MA, Mr G. Harpole

Chairwoman reported Value of Stock — £3,455
Current Account — £219
Debts — £564
Value of plant — £6,673

There were no apologies and

Mr Shutlanger was invited to join the meeting.

Proposed by G.H. that *The Story for the English* be withdrawn from circulation.

Chairman pointed out that, since only a couple of file copies remained, book had withdrawn itself. G.H. said he was all for freedom of speech (as handed down by forefathers) and substituted motion that unreserved apologies be offered any person or persons distressed by alleged statements of blasphemous beliefs or instances of such activities which could similarly be construed. Furthermore a paid insertion in *The Booktrader* should announce that all camera-ready artwork, copy, plates and proofs had been destroyed in the presence of witnesses.

Chairwoman said freedom of speech not handed down by anybody's forefathers. From Stone Age onwards freedom of speech suppressed by axe, rope, bullet and, in latter days, by High Court injunction. Asked for definition of "blasphemy". G.H. retired to consult *Shorter Oxford.*

G.H. rejoined mtg. Reported "utterance or utterances disrespectful to the Deity" and quoted instances of such from Mr S.'s book, dwelling in particular upon Thisman's habit of smashing stained-glass windows.

Chairwoman intervened declaring that shattering the odd window or two could not constitute a blasphemy. Recalled hitting a golf ball through Oldheading Church's east window with such force that it emerged through west window. Her father had cut off that month's allowance but not (as far as she could recall) for blasphemy.

Motion had no seconder.

Meeting closed at 9.45 am.

A significant detail in this report will not have been lost upon students of the adventures of the detective, Sherlock Holmes and his *The Case of Silver Blaze*. ("The dog, my dear Watson, did not bark.")

Neither did Shutlanger speak.

He was to break silence on Radio Market Harborough.

Transcript of interview by Simon Lee-Entwisle.

". . . their daily diet, daily literary diet, is breasts-and-bum picture papers. You don't agree? Then bend your ear to your own radio station's dawn to dark cacophony. What earthly use is it to tell such morons about donkey rides, booze in skins, mass-catering by magic, medical care only to be had by lowering patients through the roof – why even the NHS hasn't sunk to that *yet*.

Tell them about the Prodigal Son and they'd sneer, "Why didn't silly bugger get a rent-paid council pad and Public Assistance to stay in bed till t'boozers opened?

Take you! Yes – you! Are you Average Young Man? Don't know? Well you look average enough to me. Which church do you go to? I thought not. When did you last open your Bible? Oh you do remember nanny teaching you "Gentle Jesus meek and mild"? Well done!

Well, my lad, it wasn't like that.

Thisman wasn't on a walking holiday. Thisman was talking revolution. His Kingdom of Heaven wasn't free pre-masticated marsbars spiked with lager. *And no-one listened*. They were giggling at sit-coms. Sit-coms!

Go to your nearest cathedral and watch smug faces chanting Bairstow in b-flat, 'He hath put down the Mighty from their seats' and it sounds like a sing-o-gram invite to a Palace Garden Party.

Did you say you were an Old Etonian? God help us every one! Here — have this free Barbie-doll."

And next day's headlines . . .

OXBRIDGE SNOB SAYS BRITS DIM

To summarize this extraordinary episode in the firm's history, I cannot do better than quote Professor G. R. G. Morris-Eayers' *Postwar Publishing Trends.*

"Although it now is acknowledged that the publicity, unwelcome although it was, brought the name of Harpole & Foxberrow to notice of a wider audience, it seems that the partners neither recognized their good fortune nor materially benefited from it. But what really invites speculation is Why did Mr Shutlanger write his *Story?* This was and is still titillatingly ambiguous. . . ."

The Fathers of the City, they sat all night and day
For every hour some horseman came with tidings of dismay.

Yes, why *did* Edwin Shutlanger write *The Story?* Professor Morris could not be expected to know a deal about Shutlanger's background but others, less scrupulous, have hinted that the book's author's earlier pillorying by an ecclesiastical consistory court over his obliteration of a medieval wall-painting during his brief incumbency of Oxgodby had permanently soured him. Certainly the book's tone suggests that real or imagined slights by his clerical masters neither had been forgotten nor forgiven. And it is true that, when pressed to explain who were the "You" of his *Story's* epigraph,

> My father hath chastised you with whips. But I
> will chastise you with scorpions" (Kings I. Chap XIV)

his answers were shiftily evasive. On the other hand and on the same occasion, he did not deny his scorn for the vast elaborate establishment which, during 2,000 years, had expanded itself from a dozen homeless and hounded men.

Sidonie Braceburn's exactly researched biography, *Holy Fool,* although not completed in its subject's lifetime, relies heavily upon material furnished by his widow, Mimi Shutlanger, admittedly then in failing health. Unlike his earlier detractors, Miss Braceburn, herself a religious, examines her subject's pre-*Story* career and draws attention to significant earlier recorded incidents . . . for instance, Shutlanger's verbal report on a sermon preached by a Canon Micheldever at Tampling St Nicholas on the name and nature of the Deity.

Her account of his pre-Jordans Bank days also bears most interestingly upon the essential persona of the man. For instance, the unsubstantiated accounts by natives of the unusual ritual performed by him during his last years amongst the mountains of remote Tamele, hint that, despite his role as priest, Shutlanger may never have believed in the all-seeing presence of an all-knowing extra-terrestrial Being who, after numberless aeons of time, despatches a "son" in human form to evangelize a remote planet spinning through an infinity of space.[*]

But I have dwelt far too long upon the opprobrium and foetal speculation dumped at his doorstep after this single unwise excursion into authorship. *There is another Shutlanger.* For, to the end, the man had his supporters. During his Oxgodby years his stylish orations over the parish dead who, when quick, he could have had no more than a nodding acquaintance, were much admired. My own investigations support this. Elderly villagers told me that mourners left his Oxgodby church wonderingly declaring themselves "unfeeling wretches" as, after "harking to the Rev" they, too late, had recognized the manifold virtues of uncles/aunties/dads/mums. At her father's funeral, one woman was heard to confess that she had forgotten why she was there. . . . "The Rev made him sound like somebody else's dad." And others stated that, if die they must, then let it be in good Mr Shutlanger's time as he could be depended upon to see 'em off proper.

In fact, all in all, Shutlanger comes out rather well from this vexed episode in the firm's history. Had he insisted upon a reprint or taken himself off to one of the new accountant-

---

[*] See Canon Powlett's *Mission Years in the Tamele Mountains*, pp. 56/57. "Found his large body of converts reciting a creed, 'In the Beginning, man created God in his own image. . . .' Told Shutlanger in no uncertain terms that 'he was a disgrace to the Cloth'."

dominated conglomerates, royalties from reprints would have made him a rich man. Touchingly, his widow's explanation of this unfashionable commercial loyalty, was that her husband looked upon his writing as no more than a recreational diversion. She told Ginchy Montagu,

"At heart, Ed was a simple fellow. Many's the time I heard him declare school-teaching and me were his true guiding-lights. In fact, my dear, his second most favourite saying was 'When three or 33 are gathered together in a form-room, there am I.' And no, I shall not tell you what his *first* favourite saying was. But never a night came, but we lay down with it upon his lips.

"My Ed was more of a man than that Braceburn woman's biography made him out to be and that is gospel truth. In the middle of all that rumpus, George Harpole urged him to seek police protection or, at the very least, to slip off to Harpole's dad's farm up north. And my Ed's answer was, 'My conscience is clear. Why should I hide away? Scripture bids us go forth into the world to live and work in the power of the spirit. And that I have done. Come what may — Truth must prevail. The wind bloweth where it listeth, old man.'"

If Mrs Shutlanger's assertion that teaching was her husband's pole-star is accepted, then the final rumble of this explosive affair is the more deplorable. At an emergency meeting, Barset County Education Committee, by 37 votes to one with three abstentions, carried a motion that Shutlanger, "under the meaning of the Act" was unfitted for "the spiritual direction of little children/teenage pupils/mature/and even perpetual-students." And sacked him.

But when they turned their faces and on the farther shore
Saw brave Horatius stand alone, they would have crossed
once more.

Nevertheless it has been said that, afterwards, Edwin Shutlanger was never the same man, that the opprobrium heaped upon him threw him out of kilter. And this, I feel sure, was George Harpole's opinion. Later, in fact, much later, when after Emma's death, G.H. was leaving Bredon Hill for those final years first in Radnorshire and later (answering Shutlanger's call) amongst the furthest ranges of Tamele,* he confided in me that, for him, the real low in his publishing career had not been his own humiliating trial (of which, more later) but his concern at Shutlanger losing his job.

As I recall it, the gist of his words was, "Yes Hetty, I know that there were times when books were chucked on bonfires and their authors after them. And, with my church up-bringing, I ought to have guessed that what happened to Shutlanger would happen. Oh yes, I let him down alright. Badly! And he never complained. . . . That, of course, made it worse."

This sentiment does G.H. credit. However, Shutlanger may not have as been cast down at his rough handling by Authority, as Harpole supposed. Mimi recalled being told, "Like John the Baptist, I was a voice crying in the wilderness. But, unlike him, I kept my head."

---

* See Sidonie Braceburn's *Holy Fool*, p. 267, for an account of Shutlanger's death as reported by Piu Mngri – "He told me 'All still missis. No moon. No stars. Only candle missis. Mist Arple sit by bed. He hold Mist Sutlang's hand. Mist Sutlang shout. Dies.' Piu gave me a much-folded paper which quite certainly was from George Harpole's journal.

  Knew it was near the finish. No more than a shadow of a pulse. Then by Jove, he starts up. Stares blank-eyed at me. Cries out 'My Father! My Father! The chariots! The chariots and the horsemen thereof!'
  Then, Piu told me, Harpole wept."

Anyway, less than a couple of weeks after dismissal, Shutlanger announced that he was starting up a private academy in a barn converted and offered rent-free by Mr Fangfoss, a local magnate, whose sole stipulations had been that it must be named The Margaret Thatcher Academy and that its goal should be the inculcation of sturdy self-help (with some Cleansing of the Nation thrown in).

HARPOLE'S JOURNAL

"But . . ." I countered.

"No buts" Shutlanger said. "Look, here's my prospectus —

I shall be in sole charge.
There will be no staff-meetings.
Special terms for intelligent hardworking pupils.
No reduction of fees for families supposing
    themselves to be deprived.
Idlers, bullies and backsliders assaulted daily.
New educational theories unwelcome.

"But this rigmorole is counter to enlightened thought" I protested. "If you persist, you are in for another media pogrom and this time not from reactionaries but from free-thinkers."

"There's a damn-sight too much free-thinking going on, Harpole, and I am out to stop it," he countered. All these blasted consumers cluttering up the highways waving banners and demanding more things to consume.

Consumers must be put in their place. And their place is high-rise blocks where we can keep an eye on 'em. What else can they want that they haven't got already? They've got clinics to be born in, schools to be sifted in, jobs to occupy 'em, roads to roll 'em down to serve-yourself food bins, hygienic safeplaces to die in. It's a darned sight more than their grandads had."

"You are a recidivist" I said heatedly. "If you have so low

an opinion of them, how can you possibly expect them to send their kiddies to your so-called academy?"

"My school is not for *them*" he said pityingly. "My school will be for *persons. They* are only consumers."

(As it turned out, Shutlanger's monstrous creed was outrageously confirmed by an enthusiastic enrolment from disaffected comprehensive-school parents so that, soon, Mr Fangfoss made a second and third barn available.)

"But look, Harpole, now that I'm self-employed, I can't stand around gassing all day. And, anyway, there's a chap hanging about fretting to have a word with you. Can't tell from here whether he's a person or a consumer."

"Then how shall I tell?" I enquired sarcastically.

"Simple!" he said. "If he whines for what everyone else has, he's a *consumer.* If he insists on something different, he's a *person.*"

My visitor was the aged Vicar of Bag Sinderby, the Revd Geraint Stokesley.

"I am here," he said, "in your capacity, Mr Harpole, as Churchwarden of St Botolph's, Jordans Bank, where I spent my happiest years. I am now approaching my 85th birthday and, when my sands run out, I wish to rest in your church-yard. From my labours that is."

I assured him that there would be no difficulty at all, as we had more than enough room particularly on the shady side.* (I did not feel it incumbent upon myself to explain the implications of this, he being a Man of the Cloth.)

"Ah!" he replied, "But I am afraid that it won't be so simple as that: you see I wish to rest on my bed."

I remained silent (but with an encouragingly accom-modating demeanour) and he went on to say that, whilst still a young man, he had inherited the oak four-poster upon

* See A. E. Housman's poem, *Hughley Steeple.*

which his father, grand-father and great-grandfather had drawn their last breaths. And, except for an annual fortnight at Frinton-on-Sea, it was upon this bed that he customarily slept.

"And I am bachelor" he continued, "and because of its family associations, I cannot have our bed slept upon by unsuitable persons. Therefore I should like to take it with me."

He then paused, plainly expecting some response, so I indicated that his idea was refreshingly novel.

"It is, it is, Mr Harpole" he warmly agreed. "And I have left precise instructions with my solicitor, Mr Cairn, a most reliable and biddable man, that I must be dressed in clerical walking-out garb and the bed (with me in it) enclosed in a glass conservatory. Palings will be erected round about it: I have arranged for these to be painted a discreet shade of blue."

*Although I silently conceded that such a construction would be a minor tourist attraction and thus likely to augment our staitened church finance, not for a moment did I suppose that his proposals would be agreed by our Diocesan Chancellor, a notable stickler for uniformity of churchyard memorials and with an irrational dislike of the colour blue. However, I agreed to forward his petition to the Archdeacon whilst, at the same time, wishing him many more years of fruitful ministry. He then shook me warmly by the hand and hurried off to catch the 4.10 pm to Bury St Edmunds.

I reluctantly now saw what Shutlanger had been getting at. The Revd. Geraint Stokesley definitely was *not* a consumer. He was a *person*.

---

* As Harpole had anticipated, the Chancellor rejected the petition. However, when Emma Foxberrow succeeded G.H. as churchwarden, on Mr Stokesley's death, she arranged for the bed to be set up at the back of the nave as a tourist attraction and the body, labelled "Father Stokesley, Family Chaplain, obit MLXXVI" inserted into the Bosanquet Vault.

FROM DEPUTY ACTING ASSISTANT LIBRARIAN'S OFFICE,
TRINITY COLLEGE, DUBLIN, REPUBLIC OF EIRE
TO GEORGE BLOW

Copyright Act Edward VII (of England) 1908 Cl.xxxii

Herewith find one (1) volume (damaged). Title – *Our Jordan's Bank Church Organ, an Itinerary.* Author – Geo. Blow. Pubd. – Geo. Blow.

This requisitioned volume has reached me in an unacceptable state, viz.

> (a) one corner-crease (p. 3)
> (b) one brown stain (circular)
>   outer-back cover.

Replace with undamaged volume within three (3) days and remit £0.86 plus £0.73 (conversion charge into punts) plus £2 postage plus £3 packing plus £4.23 (conversion into punts).

G.H. to E.F.

This chap or lady sounds upset and I see the Act *does* say "Demanded books" must be in "an acceptable condition".

E.F. to G.H.

Send him/her nothing. Not even scorn.

*But the Consul's brow was sad and the Consul's speech was
    low*
And darkly looked he at the bridge and darkly at the foe.

HARPOLE'S JOURNAL

Usual Barchester rendezvous. Grace Pintle eagerly awaiting
me. Told her the last batch had riveted me.

"No more than my expectation" she responded. . . . "The
two of us being romantics. . . . And I have brought you four
more, all much in the same vein – just as riveting."

Unobtrusively tested weight of M. & S. carrier-bag. Felt
guiltily resentful and this may have caused me to adopt a
more critical literary stance. Said, "Mrs P., you and I are
friends of longstanding, putting up with so much, the two of
us back to back as it were, in Tampling days. Can I pose a little
query and no offence meant?"

"And none likely to be taken coming from you" she replied
jauntily. "Ask away. Pintle is safely stowed away in a Tesco
grab and gobble trough. . . . Not that it would make a jot of
difference if he was here: I am into Women's Lib these days –
and he knows it."

"Well then" I continued, "The both of us recall those
Widmerpools down by the Sewerage and that vile stench
they daily brought into our school. Also that gorilla Billitt
who had the confounded audacity to attack me in my own
office. As for that Neanderthal, Vincent Slope and his grotty
dad. . . ."

"Who possibly could forget them" Mrs P. remarked
simply. "Particularly what you did to Billitt with that bat you
used to keep in its special corner. . . ."[*]

[*] See *The Harpole Report*.

"Well then" I said, "How shall I put it to you. . . . Now you don't need re-assurance that, for me, your novels are addictive: I have been glued to each page – the scenes you so beautifully describe and the consumers and persons you portray (and let me say, here and now, how I wish such events had happened to me but no such luck . . .)

"Well, put it this way (and no offence meant). . . . Have you never wanted to write of Life-as-it-really-is? Oh dear me, I have not phrased that at all well I suppose. What I really mean is Life-as-it-has-been-dished-out- to -chaps-like-me? At times, believe me, not a picnic . . . life I mean. There are things I could tell you. . . ."

"Oh, Mr H." she said earnestly, "I am so pleased that, at long last, someone has got around to asking just that. (Not that I consider you as 'an ordinary chap'. I consider you to be 'an extraordinary chap'. And so does Pintle – in his own way, of course.) Because what you have asked is true. Yes, True! True! And, yes, I do know what you are getting at. And, yes, let me tell you I *did* write one about life-as-it-really-is. It was the one which squeezed itself in between Novel 11 and Novel 12. It was entitled *The Dark Side of the Street*.

And that title says the all of it. I gave that book not just the kitchen sink but the sump beneath it. It just as well could have been called *Room at the Bottom*. You remember Mrs Widmerpool's so-called lodger, the one her 13 kids called Uncle Alf, that big hairy chap, the one you told us couldn't be pinned down when you gave him a talking-to about birth control, because all he would say was that it was enough for him to get on with the washing. Or was it the digging? Well, *Dark Side* was told through *his* lips: he was the narrator. For the fear of libel, I made him a small man, a dwarf in fact and bald. But I kept in the washing. Well, you of all folk, don't need telling that life-as-it-really-was-with-the-Widmerpools would have filled a library of books.

I tore into that novel at white heat. Sent it off first-class post on a Monday. Friday, a big chauffeur-driven car stops outside the school. And there was Mr Brunt of Brunt & Badger. On our doorstep! From London! In Sawpits! I had always thought of Mr Brunt as a thin man but he was a fat man and he was all of a dither and couldn't wait. And let me tell you he didn't beat about the bush. "Oh, dear lady" he bursts out, "Oh dear lady, at last we meet. But in what circs! We received your new novel. And first my wife (who is your staunchest admirer) read it. And then Mr Badger's (who is unmarried) housekeeper read it. Now let me put your mind at rest – you have written it; Brunt & Badger will publish it. That is a sacred trust. (And this time we shall forego Publishers' Custom & Practice: the book shall appear under your own name. Oh yes, this one must appear under your own name.)

But, dear lady, I beseech you. No, no, *beg* of you. . . . Please pen no more novels in its vein. Oh no! Please! Never again! It simply is not you. Not your essential self! Dear lady, just keep on writing your wonderful, wonderful chronicles of love and renunciation and those (peculiarly your own) bitter triumphs of moral rectitude. And, if you can bring yourself to up output to three books per year. . . . And my partner who (but for an aunt's funeral would be here with me) insists that your royalties must be increased from 10% to 12½%. No, protest is useless. 12½%!"

"But, Mr Brunt"* I protested, *"Dark Side* is what life is all about. It is here, all about us in Sawpits. I have only to leave the classroom door ajar for it to seep in. If only you could conceive what goes on in Sawpits – life, I mean. Surely it is

---

* Four years later, widespread complaints from Manchester booksellers forced Brunt from partnership. Addressing a publishers' conference, he declared numerous booksellers encouraged trainee assistants to play war-games during their lunchtime breaks using slow-moving books as missiles. These then were returned to their publishers marked D (Imperfect) or F (rec'd damaged) with a Credit Demand form. "This foul practice" he said, "is particularly prevalent in Lancashire."

my duty as a creative artist to draw my readers' attention to Life – (as it really is)?"

'Yes, yes, yes, I agree' he told me (but testily). 'And it is highly creditable, very laudable, in fact. And I applaud your sentiment; it does do you credit. But, dear lady, bear in mind Custom & Practice, Publishers' Custom & Practice. There are others whose language cannot be mistaken, who can and do insist on telling us what Life is really like. Eminent authors like Mrs Cookson and Mr Amis (Junior) and, at greater length, Mr Burgess.'

'Also, let us never forget that Brunt & Badger readers already know all too well what Life is like: they are living it already. Believe me, dear lady, when they trudge homeward from the pit, the plough, the counting-house, the loom, they do not welcome Life pursuing them across their humble thresholds – they already have had enough Life for one day. Believe me, for them, life jollywell begins all too soon the minute they lay aside one of your wonderful novels.'

And then Mr Brunt recounted the terrible everyday things which happened to my readers – downtrodden spinsters patiently snatching at flying shuttles, poor old-fashioned little chaps put down by big modern Virago-reared wives, old folk hidden away by unfeeling children. 'Oh, Miss Tollemache (I was unmarried then), write for *them*' he pleaded. 'And here is a cheque in advance of royalties. Note the 12½%.'

"So you see that was that, Mr H.' she concluded, her eyes, behind her specs, brimming with tears.

When I repeated this affecting episode to E.F., she laughed heartlessly. "Seventeen, did she say? She's written 17! Why, she is spraying her drivel around like an agricultural slurry-spreader: Greenpeace should prosecute her. But OK, OK . . . if the old humbug can rattle them off that fast, then she can knock one up for you and me."

"As for Brunt, he is a monster. Publishers' Custom & Practice! How many other drudges does he keep in his outworkers' harem? He is worse than a Soho madame. If Mrs Thatcher was still at No. 10, she would bring in a bill against him and have him seen-to."

Despite this cynical outburst, Harpole's report was not wasted upon Emma Foxberrow. Subsequent events show that she had recognized that there, on her doorstep, was a high-performance fiction-machine in first-rate running order, a contraption which, exactly tuned and programmed, could turn out whatever brand of literary product time and its tastes demanded. And she immediately acted upon this.

EMMA FOXBERROW TO FELICITY FOXBERROW

"Look here" I said firmly, "How would you fancy yourself as Virginia Woolf, eh?"

"Mrs Woolf!" (she bleats). "But isn't she taken for exams? And not just school-exams . . . university exams? If it's that Mrs Woolf, I might as well admit here and now that what she writes is beyond me, so it would be hopeless trying to be her. Nothing ever happens in her books, does it? And unless something is happening, has happened or is likely to happen, I can't get myself into a book. And doze off. I suppose it comes from not having had enough education."

"Come, come, Cheer up!" (I comforted the poor old thing), "You are not the first to give up on Virginia. She is that sort of writer readers read about and don't read. But there is nothing to stop you taking over one of her spare titles. That would make a start. No-one will sue you because the title is as far as she got. And any writer, even in the grave, must rejoice in some fellow struggler picking up a throwaway title and doing something with it. And it's an absolutely splendid one

– *The Jessamy Brides*. I came across it in one of her 1920s diaries. She says that she was of a mind to write about a couple of women (The Jessamy Brides), sitting upon a roof-top, chatting about their husband, whilst awaiting an eclipse of the sun."

"On a roof-top?" (anxiously). "Oh, how original! But quite risky I should have thought. And you mean 'husbands, plural' not 'husband, singular'?"

Explain it was not a sloping roof but a flat roof. And that this pair were married to the same chap.

"One after the other? Surely not at the same time?"

Told her Virginia didn't say, so her literary heir's every option was open. Emphasised a ménage-a-trois sells better: such arrangements fascinate. And not just men . . .

"Oh no, not me! Pintle is enough for me. So long as he sticks to our arrangement – which is to stay a father-figure."

(Reflects) "Though I suppose if ever he insisted on his rites of marriage, then I might welcome another woman taking her fair share of them. Well then, I suppose if I put my mind to it, I *could* make up a long story about the three of them. But what has the eclipse of the sun to do with it? I don't like my books to come out too fanciful. . . ."

(Felix, dear girl, she was on the slippery slope!)

"And when you pull it off, overnight your name will be a household word," I slip in. "George Harpole tells me that you long for your novels to be noticed in those ambrosian fields where the literati browse. Well, with me at your elbow, *The Jessamy Brides* will be noticed all right. Oh yes, indeed, it will be noticed. And you with it. Then think how proud good old George will be."

"Yes, he would, wouldn't he" (smugly). "He is my top fan: even my couple-a-year books rivet him."

"Look to the years ahead . . ." (warming to the work). "See G.H., now an old gent, old but not infirm. See him hand in hand with his grandchildren, William and Eleanor. It is a damp Saturday afternoon. Raining cats and dogs, in fact. They enter Barset Museum. He totters along to press a nose at a familiar pane of glass labelled, THIS IS A RECON-STRUCTION OF THE ROOM IN WHICH GRACE TOLLEMACHE-PINTLE PENNED HER INTERNATIONALLY ACKNOWLEDGED MASTERPIECE, THE JESSAMY BRIDES.

"And there will be your sensible chair, your inkpot, your pink blotting-paper, a framed portrait of Mr Pintle and another of your pa, the Alderman, and a vase of faded flowers about which beholders can think what they like (upon that you may absolutely rely). And George will beckon the Curator and tell the poor chap that you would never have allowed an explicit picture like *Déjeuner sur l'herbe* on your wall. 'Her favourite picture was . . .' he will quaver . . . (What is your favourite picture?) . . . "Her favourite picture was *The Relief of Lucknow, Flora Macdonald hears the distant Pipes.* And if the Curator should demur, George will say, 'How do I know, sir, what Grace Tollemache-Pintle liked or did not like? I know, sir, because I knew her . . . intimately.' And then the Curator will invite him to lecture The Friends of the Museum on 'The Essential Tollemache as I knew her' (with slides)."

Felix, it was cream to the cat. Asks "Can't Mr Harpole's photo be on my writing table too? That farewell one he gave me, the one in his cricketing togs with that bat he kept for hitting Billitt. Pintle's photo could stop on the desk top too: I shouldn't want to hurt his feelings."

(Doubt creeps in.)

"But wouldn't all this mean that I was dead? I'm not sure I like that."

"But think – you in a museum!"

"OK" she says. "I suppose we've all got to go someday. Even William Shakespeare had to go, hadn't he. I'll write you a book if you think George Harpole would like me to. Just remind me of that title again and I'll run off something to fit it."

FORWARD TO THE BIG BRITLIT PRIZE!

FELICITY FOXBERROW TO EMMA FOXBERROW
I'm halfway through the only Tollemache mercifully on our monthly Woodeaton library-van. *The Enslaved Heart!* The Big Britlit! You must be off your noddy.

E.F. TO F.F.
But surely, even with your sub-standard convent education, you must know that, these days, it's editing makes or breaks a novel. Bacon did it for Shakespeare. And never forget the Bible was writ by a committee. She'll write it; I'll edit it. They do it all the time in New York. They push a lame-duck in at one end and it comes out a gold-egg-laying goose at the other.

And thus the scene was set for surely the most extraordinary and certainly the most exactly documented campaign ever mounted to contest Britain's most coveted literary prize.

Then he stood calm and silent and looked upon the foes
And a great shout of laughter from all their vanguard rose.

The first and, as its author supposed, final version of *The Jessamy Brides* was finished and delivered well within the 19 days Emma Foxberrow had demanded. Grace Tollemache-Pintle had reconciled her muse to coping with two heroines, of whom neither was an elementary school-mistress, deprived by ailing or accident-prone parents of the consolations of love and marriage. The story (as she was fond of telling writers-circles) simply flowed from her pen. "It wrote itself" she told them.

Although these two well-born ladies, Estella, aged 27, blonde and beautiful, and Carmencita, beautiful and brunette, were discovered where Mrs Woolf had abandoned them (seated upon a roof-top, bored almost to extinction and sipping consolatory dry sherries whilst awaiting the sun's eclipse) her literary heir quickly brought them down to earth and, in a single paragraph, hustled them off along well-trodden paths.

Her immediate difficulty was giving moral and legal credibility to Sir Bruno Jessamy (the hero) having wives-in-tandem and that before his 19th birthday. This she triumphantly achieved by making it a condition of his inheritance of title and fortune that, without demur, he also inherits the deceased uncle's widows. (Whilst panning gold in the Black Hills of Dakota, the late Sir Walter had embraced the multiple marriage arrangements of the Latter Day Saints.)

However, the author early makes it crystal clear to young Sir Bruno that he must reconcile bigamy and his baser self with a likely spell in the jug. So, with both women, he is scooped up from his Midland hunting-shire and dumped on his late uncle's property on Dakota's western frontier where too searching domestic enquiry commonly is answered tersely by a Colt revolver.

Nevertheless, still bothered by moral scruples, the author packs off Estella for an afternoon stroll down a nearby gulch where she is set upon by a grizzly-bear and devoured. Sir Bruno and Carmencita are then shipped back across the Atlantic and resume their rightful place in county society where, with a lavish grant from English Heritage, they convert Northanger Nunnery, their neglected mansion into a theme-park much visited by bored pensioners and school parties. The couple then settle down to long years of concupiscence.

HARPOLE'S JOURNAL

Told Grace her *Jessamy Brides* was much the best thing she had written. "Yes" she agreed simply, "I gave it my all."

"I have only one minor reservation" I rejoined. "For me, a single incident mars the tale – the cruel demise of Estella whilst still in her pride of life." Then explained that, if for the purposes of morality and plot, one wife must die, my nominee would be Carmencita, who struck me as a self-opinionated contentious feminist too fond of having her own way.

Was asked why I favoured Estella.

Answered she would be more of a helpmeet when it came to fixing up a heritage centre. In a managerial sense, having her as a partner, would be as good as being married to Mrs Thatcher. Admittedly, Carmencita (as delineated) might have gratified Sir Bruno's gross animality, he being only a callow 19, but you could bet your life, she would jib at taking admission-tickets at the mansion door.

"I take your point" Grace conceded. "The bear shall have Carmencita."

Later shared my enthusiasm for the novel with Emma Foxberrow who at once went off into prolonged and maniacal merriment. "At times you are quite unbelievable, George" she cried. "Come now, admit it – for you James Joyce and Kafka need never have lived. Her novel is utterly and hopelessly ridiculous."

JOURNAL

Met S. in The Fusilier. Reluctantly bought him his usual double rum. "Well I have plodded across that balderdash you palmed off on me" he said. "And I will lay you 10,000 to 1 against it winning the Britlit Big Prize or any other b***** prize. Why any ten year-old C-streamer could have knocked it up. Where is its b***** message?"

Replied that *The Jessamy Brides* was a love-story and therefore did not need a message.

"A love-story, my a***" he sneered. "Do not give me that crap, Harpole. Why, they don't get down to kissing, let alone having a good ****. Why even that poor old blatherer Walt Scott cuts nearer the bone when he has Ivanhoe chatting up Rowena in that ruined turret. Something *might* have got going between them but for the roof leaking. . . ."

EMMA FOXBERROW TO FELICITY FOXBERROW

. . . so I tell her to fly back from Fairyland and remind her it's not the Betty Trask Prize for Romantic Fiction we have in our sights.

Bleats "But I gave it everything. In my 17 novels I have never gone half so far."

Told her it read like Ian Fleming without the gadgets. Then soothed the poor thing and sent her on her way (with three single-spaced quarto pages of exhortation and reconciled to a re-write).

Astonishingly, the second draft was completed four days later. Now, Bruno, threatened by a sacked groom with exposure as a bigamist, escapes over a roof-top during an eclipse of the sun and flees alone and in disguise to South Dakota where he signs on as a dynamiter in his own gold-mine. When a tunnel collapses, he sacrifices himself to save his crew and is reported dead. However, preserved by a pocket of air, he crawls from the hole into a black prairie night.

A copy of *The Plainsman* blows across the trail and, by moonlight, he reads his obituary. This makes him lose his memory but, during a range round-up, he is found wandering in Wyoming by a cattle-rancher's wealthy widow.* She is a fine Christian woman who nurses him through his fevered delirium; during which she learns his history and marries him. But only in her secret diary does she touchingly refer to herself as "Lady Jessamy".

This hastily arranged solution pleased E.F. little better than the first version. Because of a greater likelihood of selling US rights, she did not jib at the story moving deeper into North America nor (with its possibility of a *Readers' Digest* condensation) its introduction of a "fine Christian woman".

---

* The practice of introducing an American to bolster US sales is urged upon authors by their publishers. Eg, several criminal characters were brought over from "the Californian goldfields" by Sir A. Conan Doyle for this reason.

There lacked not men of prowess, nor men of lordly race,
For all Etruria's noblest were round that fatal place.

MEMO (E.F.)

Told G. P.-T., we were not writing for either book-buyers or booksellers. WE WERE WRITING FOR THE BIG BRITLIT JUDGES who, long, long ago had left off reading books for *fun.* Repeated this.

BIG BRITLIT PR hand-out

Panel of Judges

Sir Colenso Cutling-Tebbut (Chairman) –
> lately Ambassador to Zanzambia. Chairman Govt. Inquiry into Perpetual Students. Chairman Archbp's Inquiry into incense-induced Ecstasy amongst High Church curates. Chairman of . . . etc.

Venetia Pettinger-Mordue – Professor Ego-therapy studies,
> University of Ipswich.

Joe Threddle – LitEd *Sunday Post.* Also part-time biographer.

Clemence Britling, FRSL – Creator of cult Police-Inspector
> Javert Mysteries.

Lady Michaela Brightwell-Furnessk (representing the
> common reader) – ex-model third wife of Lord Berzim, Manufacturer of Berzim's Slow-burning Stoves.

MEMO (E.F.)

Dominant panelists – *Pettinger-Mordue* – rabid feminist, contentious Radio 3 critic, agnostic Lesbian academic, well into Tang, wrote student cult-book, *Bed & Bored.*
Threddle – indefatigable seeker after significance and a CBE (but wd accept OBE or rich widow). Hates booksellers. (Dad had Wolverhampton bkshp and made him man it Saturdays.) Nomination by him as a subject for biography sd to be one of the new terrors of death.

If this awful pair gang-up, rest of panel chaff on winnowing-floor.

GRACE TOLLEMACHE-PINTLE TO EMMA FOXBERROW
It's not fair making me begin all over again. Mr Harpole told me the consummation of Bruno and Gertrude's love stirred him every bit as much as Romeo and Juliet did when he had them for his school-certif. And my verbal exchanges apropos the 24 hour timetable of the two wives sharing the one husband had him in stitches – particularly my "clever echo" of school-timetables always starting off the day with an "act of communal worship". And let's not forget Sir Walter Scott said Story comes first, last and everywhere in between.

E.F. TO G.P.-T.
And that's nine-tenths of what's wrong with it; it's too good a story. Good stories are gall and wormwood to Pettinger and Threddle. And if your's made G.H. laugh, that settles it. No novel that could wring a laugh from Harpole has ever won the Britlit. In fact, dear, no novel that G.H. could begin to *understand* has ever won it. With Pettinger and Threddle on the jury, until first Pintle and then Harpole swear they cannot fathom what *The Brides* is all about, we might as well blow the whistle here and now and go home.

G.P.-T. to E.F.

If it's smut you want, I've already put in more than Pintle can stomach. No! And that's flat.

E.F. TO G.P.-T.

Pettinger and Threddle don't want smut. They want Significance. For them Significance is All. Look, dear, there are three ways of writing a novel. You can write it so George's Aunt Estella can enjoy it. That's a "booksellers' novel". You can write it so a bookseller can't sell it: that's a "novelist's novel". And you can write it so Pettinger and Threddle believe only they can understand it. And that's this year's Big Britlit Winner.

Now, look here, do you or don't you want to be poured into skin-tight gold leaf and be pinned into a corner at parties? Do you want to find out on Kaleidoscope who you have been all these long years? And what about a Damehood coming up with the rations?

G.P.-T. TO E.F.

All right! But only because you told me to.

So, once more, an agonized Sir Bruno, his options squeezed between two brides in one bed and sharing one cell and one lavatory bucket with two homicidal maniacs, flees yet again to the Black Hills of Dakota. Once more he goes down his gold mine to succour his men. Once more . . . alas, not this time.

His burial, under an iron sky, amidst pines in a snowbound gulch, points many a hardbitten miner and painted woman towards a re-assessment of their current life-styles and we find George Harpole confiding to his Journal,

"Told Grace she had excelled herself and particularly in her moving closing passage —

". . . and now they turned from that lone grave on a far frontier. And as the surly sullen bell gave notice to the world that he had fled, many a mother's wayward son panning the bitter creeks reflected that one soiled like himself but now, stripped of sin, stood before his Maker.

Such was the passing of the last of the line of the Jessamys.

E.F. TO G.P.-T.

This might soften the heart of a hard-bitten gold-miner but, these many years, Pettinger and Threddle have made do with swinging bricks. Now please, PLEASE and for the last time, cast off the old Tollemache and put on the New Woman. We are not writing *The Brides* for love or literature. We are writing *The Brides* for fortune and for fame. And only when fortune is in your building-society pass-book and fame has gone to your head, then and then only can you do what you like with the confounded Jessamys, right down to a regurgitation of Carmencita.

Cling to this and to this alone. Once Venetia and Joe are won to our cause, they will grind remorselessly on like the heavy-duty grit grinders they are. And neither hearts nor heads of oak shall avail the rest of the Panel.

For Britling will consider that her new novel will land upon Threddle's desk for review. And Lady Berzim will feed the 107 unread novels into a Berzim Slow-burning stove, shut her eyes and pull a doctor's note over her head. As for busy-boots Sir Colenso, he'll do what he's been doing for the last 40 years – nod at everything he can't understand and be made Chairman of another Enquiry into Inquiries.

George Harpole's verbatim recollections to Sidonie Braceburn (quoted in her *Holy Fool*) of this stage of the manufacture of *The Jessamy Brides* is revealing,

> I put it down to her (Tollemache-Pintle) not passing for the grammar school. So Emma was her god to be pro-

pitiated, flattered, bowed-down-to and boot-licked. By the time that demoniac had put her through the wringer, the poor soul was ready, aye ready to dive into seas of ink and come up spouting such nonsense as Emma and the spirit gave her utterance. Oh no, I'm not exaggerating. If you weren't . . . well, I could tell you things about E.F. Listen to this. In the middle of the rumpus, I came across Pintle with an enormous black-eye.

"There's no living let alone loving with Grace these days," he lamented. I tell her she should risk a trip to the NHS – not that it would do her much good as she is going off her head. She has taken to shouting bad language in her sleep which she has never done before. And not just shouting. Kicking! And punching! And she has lost a good half-kilo in weight. . . . On the top of all that, she is not going on a regular basis to the lav. But when I hinted at that, she yelled that all solid literature was constipatory and why didn't I know that?

What do you think she was getting at, Harpole? It's not the way she used to talk in Tampling days and at Sawpits, now is it?

He then earnestly asked advice on what he should do which proves he must have been at the end of his tether, because I doubt if, ever before, he's asked advice of anyone. Then, as we parted, he whispered, "And that's not all by a long chalk. Between the two of us, she has taken to the Bottle."

And, when he'd gone no more than a couple of yards down the supermarket gangway, he turned to thrust a scrap of paper at me. "It's a page from her diary" he muttered.

> But my novels must make sense
> I told Emma. Not so she said.
> Well if I can't put sense in let
> me put in love. Least of all
> love she said Least of all love.

"It's a bad business" Pintle muttered darkly. "And it will end badly. And then, what's to become of me?"

EMMA FOXBERROW TO FELICITY FOXBERROW

So I told her to drink or think herself onto some higher perception and then jump.

"Jump where, Emma dear?"

"Out of your skin. And gibber."

"Gibber? About what?"

"Anything that turns up! That flower-pot! The bathroom! Yes, the bathroom! People go basic in bathrooms."

"But sense? What about sense?"

"For heaven's sake, what has sense to do with it? Any fathead can make sense. Half the time Shakespeare didn't make sense. His plays are full of folk drowned in Act One and alive and kicking all-comers in Act Five. Any run of the mill prof knows what kept Bill at the grindstone was psycho-masochistic fits brought on by a pre-oedipal mother. Now look here – tell me anyone you've tried reading and gave up on."

"That T. S. Eliot."

"OK! Now what do you make of this" –

*The communication of the dead is tongued with fire
beyond the language of the living.*

"Is it about Pentecost and the Holy Ghost?"

"No! Try this,"

*And the end of our exploring will be to arrive
where we started and know the place for the first time.*

"No? here's another. . . ."

"That second one . . . does it mean they needn't have set off?"

"No. Try this."

"We are born into the dead."

"I give up" she says (but cheerily). I expect it's because I left school at 14 and Mr Sykes let those who weren't in his scholarship-class only go as far as

> *"By the shores of Gitche-Goomie*
> *Stood the wigwam of Nokomis. . . ."*

"Well, there you are then: what else did you expect from TSE? Just look at the company he kept. Didn't he say, 'Words strain, crack, slap, slip, slide into incomprehension and need footnotes to keep them sidling off'?"

Now, take a few lines of TSE you can't make head nor tail of, shake them up gently for reasons of copyright and use a Pritt-stick, all the time thinking of George Harpole who is Average Man. You'll be astonished how it will up your profundity-quotient. No? Well, let's say you've still got the Brides on their roof-top,

> Estella sipped her coffee. "Was thinking . . ." she murmurs and pauses.
>
> "Was thinking" she begins again. . . . "Was thinking how the configuration of the dead is tongued with flame beyond the language of the living. Walter, for instance...."
>
> "Ah!" Carmencita replied, "Walter! Yes, that *had* crossed my mind. . . ."

You follow? Good! OK then! And, now and then, slot in some Sin, Hell-bent sin! The old original black stuff! Graham Greene nearly won the Nobel Prize on the strength of it.

And then there's always a chance of the holy ghost. You never can tell. Which holy ghost? *The* holy ghost! Her! Now and then she leans over and puts a finger on a writer's head. Only for a minute. But that's enough: a touch makes all the difference. Of course you don't know it at the time. But later when you re-read what you've written and wonderingly ask Did *I* write that? Me? Really! *Then* you know.*

---

* William Wordsworth subscribes to this assertion –
> "that serene and blessed mood . . .
> Of harmony and the deep power of joy when
> We see into the heart of things.

And thus it was that, during the next weeks, the author herself not knowing how, *The Jessamy Brides,* from being a tale of an unusual, an amiable ménage-a-trois, became something cloudy, conjectural and with an oddly pervasive smell of Sin seeping up from the bare bones of a half-buried story.

Then Blow was set to work setting and proofing the text whilst Mrs Shutlanger, at no charge, designed a selling-jacket displaying a man sitting dangerously upon a steeply pitched roof-top, fumbling two women temporarily disabled by an eclipse of the sun. Its banner shouted

BY THE AUTHOR OF THE ACCLAIMED BESTSELLER,
SLAVE OF THE GODS

"I rather like that" Grace told E.F. "Not that it's strictly true: no-one ever mentioned my early work, let alone reviewed it, so I don't see how it could have been acclaimed."

"George Harpole told you *Slave* was jolly good, didn't he? Well, that's acclaim. And, when you turn to the back outer jacket, you will find further acclaim,

**'I have never yet read a brighter and busier
study of sin in high places' (Telegraph)**

**'This accusatory masterpiece! She stares out Life
not through a glass darkly. But face to face.'
(Post)**

**'Brilliantly climacteric! At its molten core is the
Marxist view of man as a unit.' (Herald)**

Ah no! Never ask what Herald, what Telegraph, what Post."

Thus, even the longest river winding somewhere to the sea, *The Jessamy Brides* slipped quietly into proof and then into print.

And there was a great silence.

Which went on and on.

For a very long time.

FINAL DEMAND

The Bag Enderby Church Choir's Fatal Noctambulation together with the Miraculous Salvation of Thos. Leaf	*Unattributed Author*

Failure to supply this book to our privileged universities of Oxford, Cambridge, Edinburgh, Aberystwyth and Trinity College, Dublin at no cost to the above institutions will result in the Distraint of goods and chattels in or about or adjacent to your business premises at Pioneer House, Jordans Bank, Barset, equal to the amount of the above publication and, in addition, expenses incurred by us in the pursuance of our demands inclusive of fees and maintenance of bailiffs whilst resident upon the above listed premises and the cost of removal of such goods to a Place of Sale and inclusive of commission or commission charged by the person or persons conducting an auction of the goods and chattels before referred to.

G.H. TO E.F.
They mean business. After all the retail value of the book is only 75p. Let's send it.

E.F. TO G.H.
It's the usual bluff-bumph. He must suppose that because we live in the country we're country bumpkins. NO.

"Heav'n help him!" quoth Lars Porsena, "and bring him safe
  to shore,
For such a gallant feat of arms was never seen before."

As is well known (indeed it is part and parcel of publishing history), in a final selection from which the Big Britlit Prize was to be chosen, *The Jessamy Brides* was one of the five shortlisted novels. H&F received an invitation.

> "You will be gratified to know . . . etc . . . for this most prestigious of literary awards . . . etc. . . . Furthermore, an invitation to its preceding dinner is cordially extended to
>
> (a) The volume's author and either or
> (b) One husband/spouse/blood relation/friend of the volume's author and
> (c) One representative of the author of the volume's publisher and
> (d) One agent of the author of the volume."

Transcript of telephoned message from E.F. to G.H.
Amazing Grace! Under starter's orders! Drop everything. Return Jordans Bank.

HARPOLE'S JOURNAL

What splendid news! And how fitting that this prestigious honour should be accorded to Grace Tollemache in life's eventide! What an inspiration to those of us who soldier on without hope of such reward! Nevertheless, shall delay my return to base, Mrs Fazackerly (Avona) having kindly invited me to a meal in her back parlour. (I learn that we shall dine on roast duckling in sauce italienne.) She was greatly impressed when I told her of my involvement with the Big Britlit Prize and asked me how old Grace was.

(Later) Helped Avona wash up and pull out her harp from its corner.* Sang *Less than the dust beneath thy chariot wheels* and (on Avona's insistence) *Pale hands I lov'd beside the Shalimar.* Avona declared that we blended in well together.

News of the ex-village school-mistress's honour caused a great stir in the district and Ginchy Montagu's *Highways & Byways* column normally embedded in Property was moved to Front Page. I quote,

> Mrs Grace Pintle, our local scribe, now nominee for the prestigious Big Britlit, is the only daughter of the late Alderman Edgar John Tollemache, late Treasurer of the Tampling Railway Station Defence Society, Treasurer of the Tampling Conservative Club, Vice-President of the Captain Pouch† Wayside Cross Committee and Convenor of the Tampling By-Pass Pressure Group. Mrs Pintle was first pupil, pupil-teacher, uncertificated teacher, certificated (Special dispensation for long service) teacher at Tampling St Nicholas C. E. Elementary School and, latterly, Headmistress of the Sawpits Village School from which she lately retired to devote herself to literary activities. A worshipper at Tampling Parish Church, she is Superintendent of its Sunday-School. Her husband, Mr James Albert Pintle, Superintendent of Tampling Strict Baptist Sunday-School, who recently led his bride to the altar, spent his early professional career in the household of the Maharajah of Meerchawsm as private tutor to his

---

* See also Canon Powlet's report to the London Missionary Society (vol. cccii). "Harpole" he says, "was in robust voice, singing Bishop Heber's 'From Greenland's icy mountains' and 'On the road to Mandalay'. The natives were much excited by this latter hymn."

† Captain Pouch, d.1607, nom-de-guerre of John Reynolds, a Northants freedom-fighter hanged for resisting ejection from his farm during a privatisation of the local Royal Forests by James 1st. There is no known memorial to this dauntless fellow but, perversely, numerous streets, hospital-wards, schools and football competitions are named for his ejectors, the Montagus, Spencers, Mildmays, Treshams et al.

numerous children, Mr Pintle is author of *A Moral & Dramatic Approach to Problem Arithmetic* which, we learn, caused no little stir in academic spheres.

The Jessamy Brides is Mrs Pintle's 18th novel and is published by Messrs Harpole & Foxberrow at Pioneer House, Jordans Bank, perhaps better known to our older readers as George Blow's Printshop. Mr G. Harpole, the senior partner, is well known in the district as sometime acting-headmaster of Tampling St Nicholas C. E. Elementary School and presently Captain/Secretary/Treasurer of Bag Sinderby Cricket Club, Churchwarden of Jordans Bank St Botolph, Treasurer of Sinderby-le-Marsh British Legion (fully licensed) Club and Hon. Sec. of The Captain Pouch Wayside Cross Committee.* Mr Harpole is in much local demand as a baritone soloist, his forte being a pleasing amalgam of romantic and martial airs. He also plays the organ.

Sunday Herald-Despatch

BIG BRITLIST SHORTLIST BRIEFING

Vippy Siskin (*As I was going down Liberty Lane*). Last survivor of the Jack Priestley Merrie England School of Fiction.

George C. Jansen (*The Soul's White Wilderness*). Ex-Trappist monk. His novels said to be "bottled-up chatter".

Esmeralda Evans (nom de plume) (*Catch me a Salamander*). In real life The Hon. Blodwen Williams-Evans, 2nd d. of Earl of Llandrindod. Best known for her *Maid of Lucca*. Lives in Irish literary tax-haven though her earlier boob n' bum books are banned there.

Frederick Buggins (*Let Musick awake*). Has several DLitts. Those in the know say that This is his Year.

* See footnote on previous page.

Grace Pintle-Tollemache (*The Jessamy Brides*). A hack from Brunt & Badger's stable. Writes under numerous names. Novels said to read like unmade beds.

HARPOLE'S JOURNAL

Emma reluctantly decided that, since Pintle would rather watch the Big Britlit on TV, Shutlanger might be allowed to accompany us to London. Found him in The Fusilier. Immediately told, "She won't win it, y'know. Not enough hanki-panki. Page 1, Para 1, she should have laid out the three of 'em under a ceiling mirror on a king-size revolving water-bed and romped 'em up, round, down and under it till the bed burst. That said it wouldn't have made a ha'porth of difference — this chap's the winner." And he prodded an unclean thumb at a *Guardian* portrait of Frederick Buggins. "See that beard: he's a b***** seer."

Curtly told him the Prize was not for beards but for literary excellence.

"And what is more" he went on, "I have been researching at W. H. Smith's and the manager tells me it's weighing their words settles it. Showed me his weighing-machine. And Buggins's words turn the scale at 3kgm 7gms which is a good ½kgm more than the nearest. Oh yes, he's the Winner all right."

I remarked pointedly that, if weight came into the reckoning, then it would be literary weight.

"If you believe that Harpole, you will believe anything" he said. "I recall a composition old Cleggy at Pontefract Grammar School had us write and I had referred Sir Walter Scott's *Old Mortality* as a "weighty tome". (Repeated this, rolling it around like a buttered crumpet . . . A WEIGHTY TOME.) "Shutlanger weighs his words" Cleggy told the form. "See what I mean, Harpole? And I am going to write to the Minister of Consumption demanding that a book's weight must be prominently displayed on its front cover."

Was utterly exasperated. Thought, If this is all Oxford's dreaming spires have done for him, I could have done a lot worse dreaming (as I did) at Bruddersford Teacher-training College. Remarked sarcastically, "You should also insist on the author's cover weight, also his wife's and, for good measure, his mother-in-law's."

"Oh, have no fear, Buggins will win it" he called impudently after me. "That you can count on. He is the dray-horse of literature. They have loaded him with everything else from BEM to CBE. And the buzz is that there's a knighthood coming up the line with the rations. If Moses came down from Mount Sinai to submit his *Tablets of Stone* for the Big Britlit, he would be dead out of luck. This year it's Buggins's turn."

There was the usual hype to drum up a TV audience and the five short-listers were interviewed on Radio 3. Grace came last.

Radio 3 – ... and finally we come to Miss, Ms or is it Mrs Tollemache-Pintle who is a council-school teacher and is a starter from funny old Brunt & Badger's stable. Now Miss, Ms or Mrs T.-P., tell the viewers all about your novel. Did you write the book or the title first? Please be brief.

Grace – My story begins on a roof-top whilst . . .

Radio 3 – That concludes my programme. My next week's guests will be . . .

But fiercely ran the current swollen high by months of rain:
And fast his blood was flowing; and he was sore in pain.

HARPOLE'S JOURNAL (STOTFIELD MAGNA)
The book-trade being in a low state, Avona chided that my staying at The Bull put me to needless expense whilst she had the little backbedroom with a bed always made up. So, after a very satisfactory supper (poached river-trout, Jersey new potatoes with Bulgarian Sauvignon Cabernet, followed by a dessert (Mrs Tice's Mother's Forgotten Cake,* a dish until now unknown to me), Avona pulled out her harp and I sang *Roses are blooming in Picardy* and Sir Alfred Sullivan's *The Lost Chord.*† I then was given an order for two dozen copies of *Foxe's Book of British Martyrs.* Went to my bed greatly contented.

In the early hours, the wine passing through me more swiftly than I like, I groped for the bathroom but, at a corner and missing my way, I fell down a couple of steps and crashed into a cupboard which flew ajar and unloaded an avalanche of hardbacks upon me. And then itself. The next minute a light was switched on and it was Avona uttering a loud cry and also utterly naked (and, if I may say so, looking uncommonly handsome).

Then, when she had pulled me clear, so as not to embarrass her, I set to re-erecting the cupboard and stuffing back the

---

* Mrs H. Tice's mother (Mrs Leila Baker) was an 18 year-old pupil-teacher at the Consolidated School, Northfield, Minnesota, on that fatal day when Jesse James rode into town on his last raid. It was from her that Avona Fazackerly inherited the recipe for this splendid confection (which can only be baked electrically).

† Harpole is said to have had a deep bass voice which reminded E.F. of "some Muscovite singing Mass and rolling wads of words as though he was relishing an apple-pie too big to swallow".

books. But what struck me as unusual was that they were all the same size, weight and colour. (I suppose being in the trade made me notice this.) In fact, they all were *Foxe's Book of British Martyrs*. Pile after pile of them! And all in mint (See-Safe) condition!

Only then did it sink in what had been going on these past months. And, seeing this, Avona immediately burst into floods of tears and would not be comforted. (Well, not immediately.)

This morning, reflecting on this touching evidence of her affection . . . well, perhaps even love (for the books were not on Sale or Return) and its subsequent highly satisfactory consummation, I consider it no more than a proper course to ask this amiable and healthy woman to be my wife and mother of our kiddies yet to be. Having a loving and willing help-meet is much to be desired, particularly in these days of Sale or Return with everything.

Never, I ween, did swimmer in such an evil case
Struggle though such a raging flood safe to the landing
place.

HARPOLE'S JOURNAL

Our party arrived at top of staircase. Found ourselves in
beautiful but crowded ante-room with numerous portraits
of Master Butchers on its walls. Grace remarked that, now
she saw what she was up against, she felt like turning tail.
"Particularly that intellectual in a frogged smoker, the one
with the beard, that one everybody is buzzing around."

"That honey-pot is Boozed-up Buggins" remarked large
greasy-looking girl loitering in a revealing costume. "And the
busy bees are The Media, also his agent and his publisher's
sales-manager, also sundry hangers-on hopeful of his genius
rubbing off on them. The buzz is gone around that he is The
Winner, it being his turn. And I sure hope they've got it right
this time as I'm sick to hell of that leaking Welsh watermill
the Arts Council granted him; it is like dwelling in one of
those rain forests."

E.F. broke in with "This is Lucinda Tollemache-Pintle, the
acclaimed novelist and author of the shortlisted *Jessamy
Brides.*"

"Which begins during an eclipse on a roof-top" I added.

"Oh!" the girl said, not even looking at Grace. "Pleased to
meet you. As a matter of fact," she giggled, "I am Buggins's
muse (also supplied by the Arts Council . . . sort of). Though
between these four walls, what he churns out is not for me.
Mind you I have read all six books *about* him. Not that, if he
was on the run, they'd be much use as a photo-fit: he's not
one bit like biographers say he is. They should have waited
till he was dead and then paid me for a slanderous revelation.

And I have snapshots to near-enough prove it. Ah well, there's always the mill-pool. Oh no, not me! Buggins! Then I'll slim down and go back to Alf; he's into buying up high-rises and de-vandalizing them. Look, there go the judges. (No, not the Britlit lot. The Smithfield Fatstock judges lot. Our lot don't carry anything like the same weight.)"

Made our way to splendid banqueting hall with many more butchers depicted on walls. Regaled with a splendid and varied banquet. Was prevented from giving full attention to the menu by neighbour, a literary editor, who kept binding on about books. Finally was offered a cigar which, as a non-smoker, I refused. But Emma Foxberrow snatched it back for Albert Blow. Protested that Blow boasted he hadn't read a book since he left school. "What better reason for him having a cigar then" she responded tartly.

The end came quickly. First, to steady our nerves, we were given a stiff black coffee laced with brandy. Then silence. Then Sir Colenso grinned. Not mirthful schoolboy grin. Sad grin. World-weary grin. Then he shouted, "The winner of this year's Big Britlit is Lucinda Tollemache-Pintle's *The Jessamy Brides*. And sat down.

No-one cheered.

Then the literary editor clapped politely so we all joined in. Shutlanger laughed sardonically, sat back and blew up a cloud of cigar smoke through which I glimpsed Grace up on a podium.

"To write a novel" she began, "is to practise the supremest art. . . ."

"Great heaven!" E.F. murmured, "The poor old thing had a speech in her handbag."

"Music is all right," Grace continued. "But it's in one ear and out of the other. And painted portraits, what are they but mummified meat? Whereas my Dad, the Alderman, said a book is the precious lifeblood of its creator."

She then quietly fainted into Sir Colenso's arms and many climbed upon chairs and some onto tables, the better to see.

"Come on," E.F. said. "Let's haul her off-stage before she puts her foot into our future: it begins here."

And, when we'd dragged her into a Ladies Only, E.F. bent close to her ear and said loudly, "Grace, dear, it isn't a dream. IT IS NOT A DREAM. On Monday, you will tuck the cheque into your building-society. But *now* you are an empty page which immediately must be filled in; you are about to be born again.

"Have you ever shopped in Cambridge? You once bought a perky straw hat there? Splendid! And have you ever been caught in the rain without an umbrella? And did you say "Pooh! A drop of rain is good for the complexion"? You did? You did. Then you went up to Cambridge and are a philosopher. Who are you?"

"I went up to Cambridge and am a philosopher," Grace said.

At that moment a strong young man from one of the vulgar sundays bullocked his way in and cried, "Mrs Tollemache-Pintle, what about Sex. Be explicit."

"I went up to Cambridge and am a philosopher" Grace called over her shoulder as we hustled her past him. Only to be blocked by a very large fat man who cried masterfully, "Harpole & Foxberrow, now you have this little plum ripe for the picking, I shall buy 51% of your lock, stock, Pension Fund and barrel and pop you into my Conglomerate. Good – that's settled then."

"All three of us were up at Cambridge and are philosophers" we intoned. And made for the nearest tube-station.

Like Mrs Thatcher in her great days, Grace T.-P. cleverly caught on to what was the Media's role – solely to promote

127

her best interests. And, like Frankenstein, Emma Foxberrow found that she had made a monster.

EMMA FOXBERROW TO FELICITY FOXBERROW

.....oh she is unsupportable. "Everybody is wanting me" she had the gall to tell me, "I had a call from that Jilly Jessup, but I'd no sooner begun when she had the cheek to say, 'That won't do at all. Boring old Alderman Tollemache means nothing to readers of my column — except as a revolting instance of patriarchal domination. Nor does serving your time in that potty little elementary school at Sewerpots. Tell me, What do you fantasize about in bed? Speak up!'

Felix, you're not going to believe this. Tollemache slammed down the phone on that great big wonderful free advert for *The Brides,* my *Brides.*"

In fact, the only instance of lack of aplomb was her response to Radio Three's invitation to its *Booksport.* Pintle told me, "She's not just over-wrought: she's I don't know what. When I . . . well you can see for yourself." And he mutely pointed at another black-eye. "So on the q.t. I have had a word with Miss Foxberrow and she'll put her through a mock interview."

E.F. — Now Lucinda Tollemache-Pintle, tell us about your Prize-winning novel.

T.-P. — It begins on a flat roof when . . .

E.F. — But not as flat as what you've just uttered.

T.-P. — But that's what it *is* about.

E.F. — Grace, dear. This is Radio Three. *Booksport* customers don't want to hear about your book. They want book-talk . . . oh well, forget it. Look, take these back numbers of TLS and grub up the jargon. No, no, for goodness sake, never mind what it means. Just scatter it around.

128

"And it did the trick" Pintle exulted. "You should have heard her; I taped it. Now listen to this

> ". . . and my work naturally is on several levels whilst remaining a process of mannered self-purification. I am a me-person. My art is not a literary brassiere to hold contextularized boobs. And, if as you insist, my novels have liquidity, it is only because my deeper thinking is done in the bath which, in itself, has a destabilizing consequence − which, by and large, usually is considered to be a good thing, taken in moderation that is . . .

"I have to admit that it was a bit above my head" Pintle said. "But on *Booksport,* the chap kept crying 'Exactly!' 'Why, of course!' 'How enormously exciting!'

"And now she's back again to her old Sawpits self and no need to dunk a Depulso into the bedtime cocoa. And Emma has sworn that she won't be bothering her any more. 'You can take up your life just where I put it down, Grace' she told her, 'and I shall see you get a bursary from the Arts Council. No, of course not! Not for writing novels, you goose. For writing *about* them.'"

Lars Porsena of Clusium by the Nine Gods he swore
The great house of Tarquin should suffer wrong no more.

A casual reader might be forgiven for supposing that the triumphant and richly rewarding publication of *The Jessamy Brides* took the little firm to its peak of reputation. Sadly, not so. For, *sans doute,* the extraordinary crisis which shot the partners to centre-stage spotlight still lay ahead. And, like any theatrical extravaganza, it had its overture.

During the previous 18 months, Witwaterstrand ABX, the gigantic Americo-Brit Conglomerate's publishing pack had hunted, savaged, dragged down and devoured five UK independents. And, at a celebratory board-meeting, a young executive, Henry B. Tulkenhorm, suspecting demotion and exile from NY to the empire's new London colony, proposed that the approaching marriage of Mrs Nelly Witwaterstrand should be celebrated by a prestige publishing project and that this must be a reproduction of some rare English manuscript, a sort of imperial tribute from her new subjects.

His would-be executioners ground their teeth . . . and smiled.

On the instant, he telephoned this news to Mrs W. and she bestowed the choice of book upon her third bridegroom, a lusty young Yale professor to whom, for the time being, she could refuse nothing. And he asked for a facsimile of that psalter (profusely and gloriously illuminated by miniature paintings of medieval rural life) commissioned in 1361 by the Lincolnshire family of Luttrell and now lodged in the British Museum. And his bride-to-be commanded that this must be in a run of two copies — one for her young man and one for burial till the crack of doom in the Copyright Library of Congress.

A now reprieved Henry B. Tulkenhorm was charged by his employer with the execution of this project but (as was discovered many years later) he placed an order with a London printer who secretly agreed that there should be a third copy for H.B.T. as a hedge against the Boardroom revenge which inevitably must befall him.

The Company was spared no expense – handmade rag watermarked Lotheran acid-free paper, a superb scarlet, black and gold-leaf Ophir goatskin binding, five-colour reproduction of the medieval miniatures . . . and one glorious refinement, a 24pp facsimile insertion, hand-scripted and illuminated, from the original psalter. Each of the two books was to cost one and one half million dollars (with the secret copy thrown in).

And the bestowal of this lavish gift upon the happy pair (dressed as Lord and Lady Luttrell) crowned a three-day medieval feast in The Heaven Room of Mrs Witwaterstrand's European vacation mansion, Hipplewell Priory. (Minor guests, flown in by Concorde, were required to dress as swineherds and plowboys figuring in the Psalter.)

A random mention of this junket in *Manhattan Society* was picked up by *The Booktrader*. And within the week, the Procurator General of Printed Books (Stature Ed. VII) demanded free copies be sent at the publisher's expense to the libraries at Oxford, Cambridge, Edinburgh, Aberystwyth and Trinity College, Dublin.

An enraged Nelly Witwaterstrand summoned her Board to witness her outraged cries at this proposed rape of her love-token and, of one accord, they announced that they would contest the claim on home ground, in the award-happy New York courts. And both sides took up battle stations.

His civil servants confidentially advised the Minister for

the Arts that, if lost, defence costs would be at least several million pounds sterling and worse, catastrophically worse, would create a precedent likely to spark resistance from those British publishers despairing of compensatory Birthday Honours for the persistent plundering of their goods.

Nevertheless, after dinner at All Souls, the Minister was minded to persist in his demand and recent memoirs reveal that he had the backing of the cabinet. ABX countered by hinting intent of seeking a decision by the European Court of Justice on the legality of the British Copyright Seizure Act and it seems that there was pressure from back-benchers in vulnerable constituencies who protested that, with a general election approaching, to throw so juicy a morsel to the media wolf-pack would lose them their seats.

So an attractive alternative was concocted. The Procurator General was told to pick upon some scapegoat utterly unable to afford a decent defence, some small firm which persistently had defied his orders to deliver free books – and to proceed against it in some obscure court beneath media surveillance and to demand a massively punitive fine as a precedent with which to confront ABX Conglom.

And thus it was that this almighty splash in international publishing's pond sent ripples widening ever outward until, almost imperceptibly, they lapped on the book-trade's furthermost shore – Jordans Bank. And George Harpole was summoned to appear before the magistrates at Tampling Petty Sessions.

HARROWING, c. A.D. 1340.
Loutrell Psalter.

"Their van will be upon us before the bridge goes down
And if they once may win the bridge, what hope to save the
town?"

EMMA FOXBERROW TO FELICITY FOXBERROW

Oh Felix, all is awry here. Ruin stares us in the face.
G.H. is in a hopeless state: you wd suppose him faced
with transportation to Botany Bay. Only this a.m. I came
across him, head in hands, cowering by Blow's press and
muttering such bizarre slogans as "I throw myself upon
the mercy of the court" and "I am a poor man, m'Lord"
and suchlike grovel. He is taking this much worse than
that rumpus I stirred up at Sinji. This time he really *will* go
round the bend."

It was running into that ghastly fellow, Croser, did it.
He told him, night and morn, to pray that the Chairman
of Magistrates won't turn up. This Fangfoss, an ogre
surviving from the Middle Ages, continually has the
sentences he hands out quashed by the Lord Chancellor.
Only last month, he (the L.C.) overturned a 12-month jail
sentence Fangfoss gave a chap who hadn't even shot a
rabbit let alone a fox, plus an extra three months for
bearing firearms on the sabbath (under some law only
Fangfoss had heard of) . . .

There, of course, may have been something in E.F.'s suggestion that Harpole's morale was at rock-bottom. But, by no
manner of means, was he the craven she makes him out to
be. What she witnessed probably was no more than a
rehearsal of the letter which he hoped would extricate him
from present worry and future financial disaster.

A copy of this letter remains on file. In it, Harpole expresses
contrition for earlier wilfulness and promises immediate and

utter surrender of all the books earlier demanded by the Procurator General for his universities. It sensibly concludes by asking that the indictment be struck out and his prosecution called off.

His Journal records that he showed the letter to his partner who, brazenly skirting her own involvement, with acerbic interest enquired into the state of his manhood and if it was at birth or during schooldays that he had learnt a perverse liking for boot-licking.

This must have sent Harpole into a blacker slough of self-doubt which deepened into despair when a sharp note from the Procurator repulsed his plea for mercy, refused reception of the proffered books and peremptorily declared that, once in motion, the juggernaut of Law must take its pulverizing way. He was *not* told what now is common knowledge – that the Witwaterstrand ABX Multi-billion Conglomerate must be threatened, cowed, brow-beaten and subdued in the inadequate disguise of George Harpole.

IN THE NAME OF GOD AND HIS BRITANNIC MAJESTY
AMEN

In lawful pursuance of those powers vested in Us We summon you George Harpole Publisher of Harpole & Foxberrow Publishers resident in or about Pioneer House Jordans Bank in Our County of Barset to present yourself before Our Well-be-loved Justices of Our Peace and thereto answer Our Writ that you George Harpole Publisher of Harpole & Foxberrow did wilfully perversely unlawfully and criminally deny to and withhold from Us certain printed works designated to Us by Our Statute Ed VIII Cl. xxxii as gifts to Our four privileged seats of learning and one in Another Place to wit –

Pleasure Domes of Barset *Jeffrey Amis*

A Moral & dramatic Approach to
    Problem Arithmetic *J. A. Pintle, FRIH*

The Bag Sinderby Church Choir's
    Fatal Noctambulation and
    Thos. Leaf's Miraculous
    Preservation *Unattributed author*

Our Jordans Bank Church Organ,
    an Itinerary *Geo. Blow*

A sharp telephone call from Authority to the Clerk to the
Tampling & District Magistrates' Court set an immediate date
for the local bench to hear the Crown's plea.

There was to be no escape.

The Passion of George Harpole had begun.

Then out spake Spurious Lartius, a Ramnian proud was he —
"Lo, I will stand at thy right hand and keep the bridge with
thee."

HARPOLE'S JOURNAL

Feeling very low over a rum at the Fusilier's bar. Unpleasing voice at elbow. "Ah, we felt we should find you skulking here." And it was Shutlanger and his now biddable Mimi who, after looking me over like some item of grocery out-staying its recommended shelf-life, irritatingly said (or quoted),

> "So, therefore though thyself be crost
>   The shuddering of that dreadful day
>   When friends and fire and home are lost
>   And even children gone away. . . ."

and, Mr Harpole, you look much worse than that, doesn't he Shutlanger, dear?"

"Yes, by God, by God he does" said S. "Why this hangdog mien, old comrade of many a well-fought Tampling field?"

Against better judgment, told them how the shadow of the Crown's prosecution and its certain outcome hung over me and that I was missing my sleep and not able even to enjoy Wimbledon on TV. Admitted I meant to plead guilty and get it over quick.

"Plead guilty!" S. cried. "Guilty? What, *surrender?* Never! Never surrender to the b******. One defection, one desertion, and the thin line of liberty breaks."

"Yes, and for once, Shutlanger is right," Mimi added. "You are not to surrender, Mr Harpole."

"I am not surrendering" (with some asperity). "I am making a strategic withdrawal from an untenable position.

And it will be me, not you, in the dock that day and it will be me, not you, pilloried before my old pupils when *The Sentinel* is pushed through their doors next night."

"Never give in to the b***** tyrants' S. exclaimed passionately, evidently neither hearing nor understanding my simple statement.

"Yes" his wife echoed, "Mr Harpole, you must not give in (I shall omit the *******). You must outface them. Shutlanger here will defend you."

"Ha!" I remarked ironically. (As an afterthought, added a second "Ha!")

"Shutlanger has a LlB," Mimi said tartly. "You do still have it somewhere, that LlB, don't you? Yes, he says he still has an LlB and many's the time I have heard him say he'd like to use it on someone."

"I got it when I was at a loose-end after Oxford . . . whilst looking around for suitable teaching jobs" S. said modestly. "Although I must admit it didn't need much effort. All I had to do was to drop in at Lincoln's Inn now and then and eat my supper. And I had to eat it somewhere. As it turned out it got me the headship at Tampling Grammar, that thick lot of Governors supposing having a barrister as Headmaster would be a cheap way of putting down litigous parents. Harpole, my lad, leave everything to me and it won't cost you a bean. For Old Time's Sake!"

He then told Mimi to drink up and scud off home to rummage out his *Every Household's Home Lawyer* from the loft.

All this happened more than a week ago and not a peep out of him. Not that it matters: Shutlanger couldn't defend a toasted teacake. My situation is hopeless. Wonder how I can stop Mother and Dad and our Vicar getting to hear of me being had-up in Court?

As things turned out, the approaching case made only

small stir locally. Readers of *The Sentinel* were told that a local man would appear on a charge "to do with books" but, once it was known that these were "ordinary books" and not "the other-kind", even mild interest died.

Nationally, the picture was much the same but for different reasons – Media's resources were at breaking-point. There was a US/Middle-East small war which, annoyingly kept being postponed, leaving regiments of reporters kicking their expensive heels in the desert sand. There was a royal on his second or third divorce. There was a cabinet minister's son and his loot to be pursued across Spain. There was. . . . There was no-one to attend a piddling little provincial police-court.

However, the *Booktrader* did ask Ginchy Montagu to send in a para for its Odd Bin. And was answered that this just might be squeezed in between copying out bad handwriting on wreaths at a Sinderby-le-Marsh funeral and reporting the Fangfoss Shield Women's Cricket Final. (As, it turned out, the Bag Sinderby Ladies' opening bats, a pair of terribly fit gym-mistresses on holiday, batted remorselessly through the Petty Sessions hearing and a couple of hours beyond it.)

Fortunately, a lively and reasonably reliable letter from an interested onlooker at George Harpole's trial survives.

Alone stood brave Horatius but constant still in mind:
Thrice thirty thousand foes before and the dread deep
  behind.

EMMA FOXBERROW TO FELICITY FOXBERROW

. . . and pooh to you too. Why shouldn't I change my mind?
It's the one sure sign of a superior person. I said I wouldn't
go. But I did. And thank yr stars. A tale I shall unfold will
harrow up thy soul, freeze thy young blood till each particular hair shall stand on end. And all this in Tampling Petty
Sessions Courtrooms (which has a persisting smell of varnish
and dubious verdicts).

Our sole support, rallied upon two backless benches by
my old and now prosperous pupil, Titus Fawcett,* was
a ragged band of ex-customers of Harpole's Tampling school
– Fawcett's dad, Hairy Alfred, Emily Billitt and Mrs
Widmerpool's sister who whispered, "I'm here only because
I always had a thing going about Mr Harpole. But what *are*
books, Miss? Where do they come from?"

(There was Widmerpool himself but only because he was
up for arrears of maintenance.) Oh yes, and there was a
neutral non-combatant, a disorganized-looking chap, the
sort who loiters at life's outskirts waiting for something to
happen to him. I supposed that he'd just wandered in from
the surrounding afternoon. More of him later.

George Harpole sheepishly tip-toes in. Looks near-suicidal
but tremendously respectable in grave-clothes mitigated by

---

* Titus Fawcett had at least two known unusual ancestors – his paternal
grandfather (see *The Harpole Report*) and also Elisha Fawcett, a
Manchester lay evangelical and missionary (*c.*1799) who taught the
natives of Tamele the laws of God and of cricket. Too poor to purchase a
monument to this good man, they erected his wooden leg upon his grave.
In that fertile clime, it took root and, according to Sidonie Braceburn (see
Holy Fool, appendix iii) provided an annual harvest of bat willow.

the cricket-club tie which I've always supposed holds some magical property for him. Sits apart. Now and then his lips (ashen) move.

The curtain rises and so do we as the Majesty of the Law enters in the persons of Major Joplin (whose family has hunted down foxes and the under-classes from coverts and tied cottages for several generations), Miss Charity Threap (of Threap's dread thread factory) and Councillor Clegg (Allied Bobbin & Shuttle Operator's Union).

Mercifully there was no sign of the fabled ogre, Fangfoss.

This triumvirii stared with sycophantic curiosity at the pair of Old Bailey heavyweights sent by Authority to flatten us – Sir Gyles Exton-Smythe (now fondling a gold watch and chain looped around his paunch) and the obligatory costs-expanding junior barrister bumsucking his way up the legal ladder. It is infuriatingly plain to all beholders that Magistrates, Clerk to the Court (a local solicitor), Police and even Justice itself (come down from the Mountain) already were sagging on the ropes before this odious pair threw a punch.

Titus, benefiting from my liberating education, walks boldly across and says quite loudly, "Cheer up, Mr Harpole. This being a civil court, they can't hang you. . . ." And, an afterthought – "or anyone else here for that matter; the death penalty being reserved only for treason in time of war and adultery with the king's wife (but not a queen's consort)". Harpole turns head, seemingly neither recognizing his late pupil nor absorbing his message. Resumes bitter reflection on the humiliations about to be heaped upon him. Stares heavenwards (but without hope).

First case called. Seventeen year-old and Aston Martin let loose on public by drooling parents had crossed a double-white at speed. His flattened victim, parcelled into big bandage, is wheeled in. Parcel asked severely by the Major why he needed to ride a push-bike these days. Parcel utters moaning noise. Rolled briskly off-stage. Would-be homicide fined a tenner. Next case.

G.H. ordered into dock so that his persecution can begin.

"Prisoner at the bar, how say you?" demands Clerk (now revealed as fan of ITV's new sitcom, *Judge Jeffreys at Ye Bloody Assizes*). Adds menacingly, "Come my man, are you Guilty or Not Guilty, eh?"

"Guilty or Not-guilty?" Harpole falters.

"Yes, yes, man! One or t'other! That is what I asked you, so let us have no hivering or hovering." (Smirks knowingly at lounging QCs.) "We have other malefactors to deal with." (Glares at Widmerpool.)

"Well" says G.H., "Well, if you mean Did I or Didn't I send them those books they asked me for, that is the books I should have sent them and didn't, I suppose I have to admit that . . ."

Bench looks peeved, recognizing H. is about to plead Guilty and deprive them of the rare spectacle of London Law showing its paces. Thready Threep asks, "If prisoner is unsure of his Guilt or Guiltlessness, is it not the Law of the Land that he must be presumed Innocent until we have found him Guilty?"

Turns toward Harpole. Speaks encouragingly as to idiot child, "Now Harpole, my good man, do you or don't you want to be Guilty?" H. begins confused rigmarole.

"Yes, as I had supposed" chimes in Threep. "He doesn't want to be Guilty. Not yet, anyway."

"I lead for the Crown, your Worships," Exton-Smythe announces, bowing stagily and launching into long-winded more-in-sorrow- than-in-anger monologue. "This misguided man . . ." . . . "the Sovereign Law of this Land . . ." . . . "Our Ancient Seats of Learning . . ." "Envy of lesser breeds without the Law. . . ." That and such and similar cock and claptrap rattles round room.

Court takes supporting role. Nods approvingly at QC. Frowns darkly on Harpole.

"And" Smythe laments, "I understand that the Prisoner is not without some (albeit small) measure of education . . ." (consults brief). "Ah, yes, Prisoner is product of Bruddersford Teacher-training College. And has been a headmaster. Albeit no more than an acting-headmaster! And albeit that of no more than a council school, grade O."

Dashing major's fathead, Threep's bobbin-head and Clegg's blockhead now nodding away like yo-yo's. Fact is, Felix, I confidently await Clerk, coppers, Court and all to burst into a Gilbert & Sullivan chorus,

> A headmaster! A headmaster! Tra la!
> Albeit no more than an acting-headmaster! Ah me!
> And of no more than a council-school!

G.H. mutters mild protest. Commanded by Clerk to shut up. This rouses some spirit in the man because, manifestly to the annoyance of Sir Smythe and, instead of paying attention to further brow-beating, licks pencil and begins writing on back of used envelope. Beckons usher. Usher disdains him. Whereupon, to my joy and admiration, he shoulders aside restraining copper and clumps across to my goodself and thrusts missive into eager hands.

> THAT BLIGHTER SHUTLANGER IS SUPPOSED
> TO BE DEFENDING ME

Was none who would be foremost to lead such dire attack
But those behind cried "Forward!" and those in front cried
"Back!"

THE LETTER (CONTINUED)

On the instant I arise. Summon my henchman, Titus. Leave courtroom. Consult. Titus proposes pincer-movt . . . he heading for Shutlanger's domicile and me for the Fusilier bar. But ah! What do we espy up the Parish Church snicket but defaulter in person, goaded forward on point of wife's umbrella ferule! Mimi (breathless) reports discovering him loitering guiltily in the Fusilier's snug and having the cheek to lie that he supposed the hearing was same day, next week. Shutlanger is wretchedly disguised in pin-stripes from some forgotten wedding and so tight as likely to unman him, a soiled white tie and tattered university gown. Mimi reports, "Part is his and part is borrowed from the Operatics' clothes-basket. Wig was last used in *Iolanthe*". (Punctuates this news with absent-minded ferule stabs at husband's backside.)

Cries passionately, "Get along now, you horrible coward!"

Titus flings open courtroom door.

Theatrical entry. Much disarray, disbelief etc. Several minor performers stand the better to see. Shutlanger sways gently in a breeze of disapproval. Supports self on door-knob. Backs off. Foreseeing flight, I snatch umbrella. Stab tightest part of pants. Mimi Shutlanger hisses, "You hulking big booby! A fine friend to poor George Harpole you turn out to be! Mess things up and, as God is my witness, I'll turn you over to Alcoholics Anonymous."

Unusually large, handsome and much bejewelled woman turns up. Explain to her that Shutlanger is our defence counsel.

"Don't seem overly eager to get to work" woman remarks. "Not enough dollars in it for him, I guess."

She anchors both hands on S.'s shoulders and, one knee on his bum, cleverly shoots Shutlanger into courtroom.

"Who is this man?" Sir Smythe demands, scornfully looking S. up and down. (Ponders whether, when he's finished with Harpole, he'll have time to toss Shutlanger upon scales of justice on blanket charge of General Disreputability.)

"It is the sacked Headmaster of a local school, Sir Gyles' Clerk whispers obsequiously."

Titus draws my attention to Mimi, now flat on pavement. Bend to suggest she'd be comfier on sofa at home. Promise faithfully to drop in and tell her final score.

But answer came there none.

Stage groans, eye-flutters. Sits up. Asks irritably, "Do you not see who it is?"

"It? Who?"

"Why him! That barrister bigwig! Do you not see that he is that terrible Big Sixth-Former who ran off with me when I was an empty-headed young thing not long wedded to Shutlanger (who was his Headmaster) and me not knowing what was good for me? In those days, they called him Bert Smith. But I heard he wed some Hon. Money-bags." (This bitterly.)

Bursts into tears. Recovers. Adds calmly, "If Shutlanger spots who he is (not that he will, the state he's in) he will do him in. Oh yes, never doubt it – he-will-do-him-in. Many's the time he's told me . . . only last Sunday on our longer lie-in, as a matter of fact . . . "Mimi, should that vile scoundrel who sullied our marriage cross my path, I shall strike him down like a dog. And I shall b***** swing for it and die a happy man."

"But is not that most unlikely?" I hint. "In open court? Irrefutable witnesses abounding? Not to mention General Public?"

144

"The General Public came with me" Titus intervenes. "And even if Mr Shutlanger litters the beak's bench with that chap's brains, they'll swear a thunderbolt did it."

"Well he won't recognize him. So it can't come to that" Mimi says. "After all, apart from looking down on him amongst 400 others at the Communal Morning Act of Worship, my husband was not on such intimate terms with Smith as I may have been. All I ever recall him saying was that Smith at best was no more than London School of Economics' material."

"But there's one thing" she adds evasively. "Shutlanger may not remember Bert Smith but he *will* remember the gold watch presented to his, Shutlanger's Grandad for Fifty Faithful Years in Swindon Engine Sheds: I gave it to Smith whilst in a fit of euphoria. We just must hope no-one asks the time."

Re-enter Courtroom. Squeeze self between big American woman and the hopeless-looking chap (of whom, more later). Chairman asks Clerk if Shutlanger can defend Harpole.

"No, of course not" rat answers.

"Most certainly I can," S. says mildly. *"See Queen Anne, 1703, Vol. xxxiv, section xxi, Crown v. Sir Valerius Dedlock, Bart."*

Cannonball return of service floors Bench, Clerk and QCs (who had not thought to burden themselves with a law library). S. thus encouraged to lie on without shame, "See also *Appendix lv, Judge's opinion, Haversham v. Gargery, 1856."*

At this stage in history of British jurisprudence, Mrs Tollemache-Pintle enters wearing dark glasses. Seats herself on shooting-stick. Takes out shiny black notebook. Court uneasily foresees itself displayed in belittling light in next bestseller.

Chairman, coming-to from dreams of days better spent

slaughtering wildlife and no questions asked, declares he is satisfied Shutlanger can be heard and that Sir Gyles should proceed. ("To even more barefaced effrontery" Mimi whispers.)

An encouraged Shutlanger now bends reproving eye upon Clerk to the Court. "Ah!" he says, "Paxton, eh? Paxton G.H.? Sixth Form Soft Option Social Studies, eh? Was there not some little to-do about a gymslip, Paxton? Or worse — perhaps? A spencer? With some girl inside it? Glissa Jipps, Head-girl, High School, eh Paxton? Yes, I see we have the right Paxton. East Grinstead Poly wasn't it Paxton — after a third run at A-levels? Was it not the great Dr Johnson who remarked that the last refuge of a scoundrel is the Law, eh Paxton?"

"Your Worships, I protest" cried Sir Smythe. "This is gross contempt of a Court Officer."

"Of fiddle-de-dee" roars back Shutlanger. This splendid riposte augmented by loud cry from constable set to guard door, now flung violently back to let in hairy-faced monster on the run from Barset County Anthropological Museum.

Emily Billitt whispers, "You'll be OK, Miss. Just sit tight. No, Mr Widmerpool is not going to interfere with you: he is crawling beneath us only because he knows it is The Moor for him this time. This is Mr Fangfoss.

But hark! The cry is "Astur" and lo, the ranks divide
And the great Lord of Luna comes with his stately stride.

(LETTER CONTINUED)
Oh Felix, how I dearly wish you might have been with us. In an instant, in the twinkling of an eye, what was was not, what not was. And the odious Clerk, scenting change in the wind, cries "All rise!"

And so we did whilst the Bench hutched-up to let Mr Fangfoss into its midst. "Thank you, Gidner" he growls in direction of the hopeless-looking chap sitting next me. "Only just come across the note you pushed under my front door. Wife's sister found it. Only use that door on the Sabbath. Now we'll start again."

"But you can't do this" Sir Smythe complains.

"Can't?" (Fangfoss menacingly) "Can't! My Court, sir, can do whatsoever it thinks fit, sir. We, sir, are not hirelings, *paid* to sit here. You, sir, and our officers are here as day-labourers. You are here sir, only because we pay you to be here to perform those duties that we ask of you, sir. Sit down, sir.

"Now Paxton, you can tell us what this chap is doing here (nodding at Harpole). Looks respectable enough. More like a preacher than a poacher. Seen him before somewhere. Must be local man."

Charge read again. Clerk sneaks, "Last time, your Worship, he pleaded Guilty. I have counselled him to throw himself upon the mercy of your Court."

Shutlanger shouts "Not Guilty! And I represent him, don't I Harpole?"

G.H. gazes piteously at me. I nod encouragingly till see it is another person he gazes at. (A homely looking creature who must have crept in to stand modestly at the back.)

"Yes, your Worship, he wants me to defend him" Shutlanger says. "Look – he's nodding, your Worship." Then tells Sir Smythe he can have first go.

Encore catalogue of Harpole's depravity. Homely looking woman behind me boldly calls. "Never! He is a *good* man, your Worship." (Harpole nods his thanks. Lips move. Probably is mouthing "Yes, I am a good man."

"What is all this argy-bargy about him having been an acting-headmaster got to do with it?" Fangfoss asks. "He's not being had up for Education, is he?"

"Are you?" he growls at Harpole. "You're not had-up for Education? And, while we're on about it, what about corporal-punishment in schools?" "Ahhhhh" mutters Harpole.

"And that's my view" Fangfoss agrees. Turns to QC, "Anymore you want to tell us?"

"That is all" Sir Smythe says sourly. "Enough time has been wasted by irregularities. Which will be brought to the attention of the Lord Chancellor. Here are copies of Authority's demands delivered to the defendant with attestations that they were neither answered nor acted upon. And, when Authority's final order to deliver or be arraigned was presented, this man's reply was . . .

(Takes piece of paper from stooge.)

> I won't give you my books. If those universities want our books, they can do what everyone else has to do and pay for them. I never heard of Tampling Thread Factory being told to give away thread to university students for their flies to be sewn up to curb promiscuity . . .

(Charity Threep sniggers.)

"Now Harpole did you write that?" Smythe shouts.

"How can he say if he wrote it, your Worship" Shutlanger

butts in. "My learned friend hasn't shown it him. I expect it is a forgery."

(Paper passed to Harpole.)

Shutlanger mouths "No"; Harpole answers "Yes".

"How do you know it is not a clever imitation of your handwriting?" Shutlanger insists.

"I wrote it. And I signed it" says Harpole (his blood up). "What is more I'd write it again. And, next time, in red ink. In CAPITALS. *And* underlined!

"Ah!" Smythe cries triumphantly and has the confounded cheek to leer lasciviously at Mimi who, to her credit, returns basilisk glare of scorn, succeeded by bright beam of cloying love at Shutlanger.

Felix, do not flag: we are at the nub of things.

Mimi whispers. "Time we put some fire into Shutlanger's belly: the booze is wearing off."

She scribbles.

THAT QC . . . DO YOU NOT SEE IT IS THE BIG SIXTH-FORMER I BETRAYED YOU WITH WHEN I WAS A SILLY LITTLE EMPTY-HEAD? ASK HIM WHAT TIME IT IS BY YOUR GRANDPA'S WATCH, THE ONE THE GWR GAVE HIM.

Emily Billitt delivers same.

Shutlanger (withdrawal symptoms now manifest) peers at it. Does not utter strangled cry. Metamorphosis! (More or less means deep spiritual distress heralding change, Felix.)

"Now" Fangfoss says, "It's your turn to have a go."

"Ah, yes" S. agrees, glaring at Sir Smythe's waistcoat, "Now indeed it's my turn. My learned friend, why are you here? Here, amongst us simple Barset folk? What – No answer? Then let me tell the Court why you are here. You are here because you have been sent here by your masters to harass a

Barset man, George Harpole here, Cricket Club Secretary, Churchwarden doubling up as Organist, all of which amounts to him being a God-fearing man. Isn't that so, Harpole? Yes, your Worship, he says he is a God-fearing man.

"And why have they sent the two of you? And that Rolls lolling at the kerb? Plus the chauffeur. Your Worship, I shall tell you why. It is to heap up costs to distress my client so as to bring in the bailiffs to distrain this poor man's meagre goods, to take away not only his reputation but his roof. And this lavishness to be lumped upon our poll-tax, your Worship. Is it small wonder that those who sent their underlings here also propose to remove rating-immunity from agricultural buildings and subsidies from sugar-beet. And this whilst our thread industry is stretched to breaking-point and EEC syndicates roam our coverts to gun down the last Barset fox and pheasant?"

(The police edge away from Smythe.)

"Is freedom dead in this once great land?" Shutlanger bawls. "If this day we surrender to this pair's impudent demands, tomorrow they will be back to plunder not just our books but our potatoes, bobbins, shotguns . . . and (who knows) next week – our wives."

"Your Worships, if there is justice still to be had in Barset, let not these parasites plunder this poor man's books."

(Profound silence. Deafening clock-ticks. Felix, my girl, shades of Barset prophets, priests and martyrs throng the Court . . .)

And this goes on and on as Shutlanger wrestles with knot in red ribbon round a scroll. Makes normal hash of it. Titus Fawcett bows to Bench, to Shutlanger, to Harpole. Snips ribbons with handy pair of nail-scissors.

Released scroll whooshes down.

"Magna Carta!" trumpets S. "'Magna' meaning 'Great . . . Carta' meaning 'Charter', your Worships! Magna Carta!

Bulwark of every right-minded Englishman from times beyond mind and memory."

"I shall now construe Clause XCLIII. . . ."

"Hic erat" . . . "hic" meaning "Here", "Erat" meaning "was". "Hic erat" − "Here was" . . .

"Let's have it without the varnish" Fangfoss orders.

"M'Latin's not what it was once" Shutlanger mutters, "but I'll have a shot at it,"

> "To all . . . to all . . . freemen of Our Kingdom greetings. We here yield assign bestow bequeath to you and to your heirs descendants futurity posterity. . . ."

(Looks round apologetically. Focuses on Harpole. Mutters, "You understand, George old chap, that their lawyers didn't want any gaps for skivers to wriggle through, so every synonym blocks another hole. That's why there's no commas. It's not the same thing five times over . . . if you follow me.)

> ". . . all those liberties herein writ set down inscribed promulgated to have and to hold from this time forward and forever. . . ."

("Covers just about everything, y'see George. Dots the i's, crosses the t's.")

Then turns to Fangfoss. "It all boils down to saying The Government is a party to what comes next, which is the nub of things, y'Worship . . .

> "No constable royal officer or any person assuming appropriating possessing himself of our Royal Authority dominion regency sway."

(all of which means *you,* y'Worship and here comes the interesting bit and, George while we're on about it, I bet you never knew there were all these words for plain thieving.)

> " . . . shall seize take possess himself of sequester subtract

confiscate lay violent hands upon by any manner of means the moveable goods baggage cargoes appanage merchandise. . . ."

(Your Worship — "merchandise" meaning "goods for sale" such as turnips, cotton-reels, shotguns and books. Definitely books. You'd say books were merchandise wouldn't you, Harpole? Yes, he says they are, y'Worship.)

". . . merchandise and in particular books hereditaments messuage trappings . . . from our loyal subjects. . . ."

(Do you suppose yourself to be a loyal subject, Harpole? Didn't you tell me once you were in the Territorials? Yes, he says he was. Your Worships, He says he was a captain. But, even if he hadn't been a captain, even if he'd been only a private in the Pioneer Corps, it would have been just the same because it goes on to say, "Whatever his estate".)

". . . loyal subjects whatever his estate without that man's consent agreement acquiescence endorsement yea even . . . ."

"That's enough of that" Fangfoss growls, "We're not block-heads: it's plain enough put and what's good enough for our great-grandads is good enough for us. Case dismissed. Any costs to Harpole here. Like a lift back to Sinderby, Gidner?"

But now he feels the bottom. Now on dry earth he stands.
And round him throng the Fathers to press his bloody
*   hands.*

But that is not the end of it, Felix. Oh no! The Bench troops off-stage, Widmerpool flees, Harpole walks free, Shutlanger strolls across to his learned friend. Says he, "And by the way Smith, under the heading of 'Dower, hereditaments and appanage' read also 'Watches'. And, laying an unlawful and restraining hand upon that barrister's chest, with the other gives an almighty tug. Waistcoat buttons spurt.

He then turns to his Mimi. 'Here, dear' he cries triumphantly, 'Look here, sweetheart. This day is a turning-point in our lives' and, holding aloft the big gold watch, 'Now, at precisely 4.10 pm railway-time, and at long last, I know I'm every bit as good a man as Grandad.'

Felix, my girl, it had been a long and wearisome day but it was not yet done. The unusually large lady from America who had kick-started Shutlanger down duty's path, tapped my shoulder. 'You are Emma Foxberrow of Harpole & Foxberrow, General Publishers, Inc. And I am Nelly Witwaterstrand of ABX Giant Conglom come here to take you under my wing. Not that I do not know that you have a healthy little business, dear, because, earlier on today, I was shown round it by your young feller, Blow. Also Emma, I can see that you have spunk. And I am a great one for spunk. Spunk is what I most admire. My third chap, that prof from Yale, lacked spunk.'"

And, Felix, as she remorselessly went on and on, I knew that I was witnessing a most extraordinary phenomenon of maxwellian magnitude. *She* swelled and the courtroom *shrank*. Great heaven! I thought, she is going to explode and us with her or, when these four walls meet, we must all smother and be suffocated. And this in our Hour of Triumph!

And then (but do not be alarmed) I swooned because, when next I heard her, she was saying, "Well, that was real painless, wasn't it honey?"

And I was holding a quarter million dollars. "And" Nelly adds, "For good measure you can toss in that young feller Blow: one way or another way, I shall make a man of him."

Felix, she was out of this world. But it was no dream. Come daybreak and from my bedroom window, what do I espy but two pantechnicons loaded with Harpole & Foxberrow's lock, stock and barrel right down to the degenerate Blow. "Miss Foxberrow, Miss Foxberrow!" he called piteously, "Miss Foxberrow, I am being taken off to America. Why? Why?"

Then they were gone.

All gone! Very sad! But wasn't it top-hole whilst it lasted? Better, in fact, than Sinji! But as the school hymn went . . . (you can't have forgotten).

> We blossom and flourish
> As leaves on the tree,
> And wither and perish.
> But naught changeth we.

Then I looked around for George Harpole to give him his share of the loot and the good news that his days of toil and travail selling books were done.

But he had gone too.

POSTLUDE (LARGO MAESTOSO)

But when above the surges they saw his crest appear
Yea, even the ranks of Tuscany could scarce forebear to
cheer.

"but he had gone too. . . ."

Yet what a time to go!

For now, with a fair and following wind, Emma Fox-berrow, basking in a bookish high-summer, could swan off to Cheltenham, to Oxford, to Bath, to the South Bank, to lecture festivals on Success. Top editors would defer to her opinions, property billionaires turned Conglom Publishers would take her to pinnacles of power and say, "All this, a CBE and three DLitts will I give thee to make my Sappho List outsell Virago. For I am the very Devil."

But George Harpole had gone.

For his heart had never been in commerce and, although he never said so, he had looked upon the accumulation of wealth as a vulgarly unsatisfactory pursuit practised by morally unsatisfactory persons. And how well I recall him saying, "Hetty dear, . . . we're not here for all that long you know. And when we wander off (as we must) into the dark, all we shall take out is what we came in with − our innocency (if there's any left). Well perhaps . . . anyway, that's about all I have hope for."

Even before the humiliation of a prosecution, he must have hankered after the untrammelled live-and-let-live life Mrs Fazackerly now held out to him. For it was about this time that her uncle, a long-retired master of a Hull whaler, died, leaving her his commodious villa by the Wye at Builth Wells and his considerable savings to maintain this in style.

It may be . . . (but who knows? Nothing's so secret as

what's between husband and wife) . . . it may be that they never loved deeply. Yet they got on very well together. Let's say that each admired the other, that their bearings were set towards a general amiability, that each had a liking for the steady plod of marriage, that each had a taste for that prime ingredient of domestic felicity – *each listened to the other.*

So they wed and set up housekeeping together.

I fancy that Emma Foxberrow, lost in herself, did not see what was afoot till too late. Many's the time I have brooded on the whys and wherefores but it is as baffling now as it was in those long gone days in Brum, when I was Rose Gilpin-Jones's companion-help and, coming in from the night, paused by the longcase clock to wonder at poor old Miss Foxberrow's maunderings as she lay abed in Room One.

But even then, though I was no more than a silly 18-year-old sixth-former and, similarly, overly full of myself, even then I guessed that, long before in early womanhood, she had been offered contentment, perhaps love and had let these pass her by. For I do believe that she might have learnt to love George Harpole as, once, he had loved her. But at Sinji and, later, at Jordans Bank, there was no room in her heart for anyone but herself. Well, she was not the first and, as I know too well, would not be the last to snatch too late at happiness as it flies.

Later she knew. Oh, there's no doubting that. But then, years later on Bredon, her pride of life was past, its passion spent and, like the last light on Malvern's hills, only the lingering late evening of love . . .

But I am straying into sentiment and silliness . . . alas, and into alliteration. And this is a book about books and the business of books. For Emma Foxberrow, James Alfred Pintle, Gidner, Grace, George Harpole, Mimi, Mr Fangfoss, Mrs Witwaterstrand, Avona Fazackerly and Edwin Shut-langer slip and slide like shadows, are moody, unreliable, bothersome. They flounder about and need footnotes to keep them from sidling off. Whereas books have body; books (if you are listening) always will say what they said last time. Or stay silent when you shut them up.

Anners,
Cransley,
April 1992.